"Nurses will save the world! I heard that from a friend many years ago, and this year I am beginning to believe it. This is the fourth fabulous book that I have read this year written by a nurse. Ellen Swanson has added to the works of Lucia Thornton, Teddie Potter, and Mary Jo Kreitzer, and all of them show us the way to a more holistic, collaborative, and partnership approach to health and to life.

Swanson's unique niche is how she uses beautiful mandala graphics to merge the linear, head-centered components of life with the circular, heart-centered principles. In every chapter, whether discussing business, health care, education, or knowing oneself, Swanson helps the reader to understand the circular paradigm and all of its practical applications. She then makes sure the reader can apply the book's wisdom by following each chapter with some hands-on exercises.

This book offers an excellent template to help us move from a dominator society to one that is more collaborative and heart-centered. I highly recommend it for every classroom and every professional."

—Bill Manahan, MD, assistant professor emeritus, Department of Family Medicine, University of Minnesota Medical School, former president of the American Holistic Medical Association

"I think what impressed me most upon seeing the mandala was how powerful it was. It was as if you had taken my thought process, my brain, my way of thinking, and made it visible. I am a very deep thinker, intuitive thinker, analytical thinker—and conventional ways of thought have never addressed that. Your concepts gave me goose bumps."

—Jeanne Stephan Kiel, student nurse

"Ellen Swanson, my dear friend and colleague, has written a beautiful guide to living deeply, mindfully, holistically, and circuitously. She shares these insights through metaphor, story, and personal experience, gently inviting the reader to participate in a transformational process. I love the idea of being a "messy mortal" capable of great love, compassion, and peace, especially when being nudged by such a beautiful spirit. This book is a gem and may well be one of the guides to the organization of truly integrative health care."

—Mary B. Johnson, PhD, RN, AHN-BC, CHTP, professor eⁱ **…us, St. Olaf College, f**ᵃ**lty, Center for Spirituality and Healing, University of Minnesota, …stic Nurses Association, board membe**ʳ **r at Pathways: …ter**

"Thank you from the bottom of my heart for that class on Sunday. It really was one of the most personal life-enlightening events I have ever attended. To be able to look at my life in that circle and start to make the connection of how and why different events interacted and affected my life was both overwhelming and magically cathartic all at once."

—Robert Dunn, mandala workshop participant

"Ellen Swanson has written a beautiful, touching, and visionary book on the deep strength and inner wisdom within all of us if we can let go of old ways of understanding power and control. Her book provides a pathway to more creative and effective life in so many settings. It is a must read for those committed to building a more peaceful world, within our own lives and in the global community."

—Dr. Mark Umbreit, director, Center for Restorative Justice & Peacemaking, University of Minnesota, author of *Dancing with The Energy of Conflict and Trauma: Letting Go–Finding Peace*

"This excellent work of Ellen Swanson leads to the way of harmony and peace in the world."

—Mohammad Mohi-uddin Khan, professor of Indian Religions & Urdu Language, Mohammad V University in Rabat, Morocco

"I was deeply grateful for the opportunity to experience the mandala labyrinth, especially with Ellen Swanson, its creator, as my guide. This magical tool holds endless potential for healing—not only for individuals, but for communities and cultures—through its ability to reveal patterns, themes, and other amazing discoveries. I will definitely consider it a valuable addition to my professional and personal toolbox."

—Katherine J. Pohlman, RN, MS, JD, nurse, attorney, coach, and consultant

"Heart, Gut, Head: Creating a Healthier Hierarchy is a rare book that provides a construct for a new way of being that so many people practice already, and others are hungry for. Within these pages lies a tool that can be used to aid growth toward a realm of collaboration and peace. The tool gives voice to the many and the individual and, in doing so, enhances our capability to transform our world and health-care system. If you are ready to feel the heart of holism, read on."

—Stacy Miorana, RN, BAN

Heart Gut Head

Creating a Healthier Hierarchy

ELLEN E. SWANSON, MA, RN, BSN, PHN, HNB-BC

ISBN 13: 978-1-59298-872-3

Library of Congress Catalog Number: 2015906074

Printed in the United States of America

First Printing: 2015

19 18 17 16 15   5 4 3 2 1

Beaver's Pond Press
7108 Ohms Lane
Edina, MN 55439–2129
952-829-8818
www.beaverspondpress.com

To my parents, H. Ralph and Elizabeth Hernley,
who in retrospect endured more challenges
than I can imagine, and were incredibly brave.

TABLE OF CONTENTS

Foreword

While many try to break loose of the traditional, hierarchical ways of relating to others, they often lack the knowledge, skills, or attitudes necessary to make the change. Ellen Swanson's model emphasizes a circular process that allows individuals the time and opportunities needed to build relationships that have transformative potential for both members. She encourages health-care providers to model their client's world and compassionately plan and implement interventions that are consistent with the client's world view and current needs. She also shows how this can be done in many other aspects of life by people outside of health-care fields.

Through case examples, she informs the reader that it is essential to stay with the client's world view until they are ready to change or grow. This ability to *pace* before leading is basic to her model, but too often not understood by providers. Instead, many try to *lead* their clients to new behaviors or attitudes before they step into their world view and engage them at that level. By pacing first, Swanson illustrates how to help clients build the internal resources they need to grow, change, and cope with daily life. She states that the "process dance" provides the members multiple opportunities to retain what is helpful, and reframe what is not, both as individuals and as partners. Her case examples illustrate the importance of the *dance* as a way of creating *trusting, functional relationships* needed to facilitate growth and healing—the first aim of intervention in the theory named Modeling and Role-Modeling. For those familiar with the theory, Swanson's work also builds on the other aims of the theory, illustrating the processes of modeling and role-modeling.

Comments such as "When we blame, we stagnate," or "differences in perceptions...are opportunities for increasing healthy intimacy," or "shared good intentions forged a unity" are included throughout the text, elegantly planted so the reader can learn and absorb. I particularly love her descriptions of *quiet, caring wisdom* held by those who set intent to care and heal, and how individuals can tap into this sense of self and use it purposefully. Her *body memory* reminds me of Ernest Rossi's *state-dependent memory* and

Rupert Sheldrake's *cellular memory*. Both authors hold that there are cellular responses to situations that stimulate the individual's unconscious memory to recall similar past experiences. Because the first experience triggered chemical responses, the unconscious memory of the experience triggers the same responses. Since it is at a cellular level, it is experienced as intuition or body memory, often identified as a "gut reaction," or "feeling." Swanson indicates that this type of *wisdom* enhances the provider's ability to work within the client's world view.

She also alludes to the importance of learning to attend to messages from the universe—messages that help her follow her own instincts, affirm her purpose, grow, and heal. Her message to the reader is to learn to believe in oneself, to embrace the essence of self, and to know that persistence will produce outcomes. She provides ongoing self-reflective exercises for those who wish to experience insights, learn about themselves, and become more fully "perfect," that is to say more fully loving and compassionate with others.

Her final chapter provides the reader with a philosophy that she calls "My Nice Creed," that specifies a list of fifteen ways to contemplate the wonder of life. This in itself is worthy of putting this book in your "read often" pile. All in all, this work promises to help humans find more satisfying and effective ways of being, and being with others. It is applicable for individuals or two or more in any setting. The messages are subtle, but clear. Trust, take risks, set intent, stay focused, and enjoy the outcomes. *And so it is.*

Helen L. Erickson, PhD, RN, AHN-BC, FAAN,

Preface

Sometimes we find ourselves in boxes such as those set forth in the traditional, hierarchical organizational chart. I want out. Don't you? American systems theorist, futuristic architect, and author R. Buckminster Fuller (1895–1983) said, "You can never change things by fighting the existing reality. To change something, build a new model that makes the existing model obsolete." What if we build a new model to help us get beyond the boxes that limit us?

Heart, Gut, Head: Creating a Healthier Hierarchy moves us past the boxes and into the twenty-first-century circular concepts of joining and connecting instead of correcting; collaborating and contributing instead of controlling; and welcoming and encouraging instead of excluding.

How can we visualize these holistic, circular concepts without excluding the linear? How can we have both/and instead of either/or? How can the circular dance with the linear? Readers will be inspired to identify when the box step is needed, and choose whether or not to dance it.

Heart, Gut, Head: Creating a Healthier Hierarchy explores the two paradigms conceptually, visually, and through storytelling, including how we can consciously begin the deep healing process that is needed for the two models to work together in a compassionate manner. For deep healing to occur, compassion is necessary. Compassion comes from the heart, which in a literal sense is the circular center of our bodies and in a figurative sense is the core of our ability to relate.

Introduction

Holistic philosophy concept featured: resonance

It is unwritten. I call it life's little instruction manual. Every generation contributes a chapter. One memorable entry is a television program entitled *Father Knows Best* (1954–60). I experienced the dominantly male perspective portrayed on the show in real life through the parenting norms of that time, a strict religion, the public and private educational systems, and in the "Doctor as God" approach in health care, since most physicians at that time were male.

In the early 1990s, while studying the theories of Austrian psychotherapist Alfred Adler (1870–1937), I became intrigued with his notion of "two ways of striving." Adler identified these two ways as "striving for superiority" and "striving for perfection" (Manaster and Corsini, 74–6). I understood his work to suggest that there might be an option other than male dominance. Perfection sounded like such a loaded term. I tried to figure out what he meant. I concluded striving for perfection was really about striving for self-growth, more of a nondominator perspective. I expanded my understanding of striving for superiority and striving for self-growth (perfection) by listing some characteristics for each way of striving. I gleaned additional useful perspectives from the works of other experts in the field and a variety of holistically oriented publications.

The characteristics of striving for superiority fit the traditional organizational chart in which each person in an organization is represented by a box. The boxes are then arranged in a linear vertical fashion, based on levels of authority and accountability. This traditional linear template for organizational charts is a visual embedded in Western culture; we carry it in our minds and apply it consciously and unconsciously in all aspects of our lives. It often conveys a message of being either "more than" or "less than" others.

In contrast, I discovered that there's no mental template that corresponds to the striving for self-growth concept. For fifteen years I tried to envision what that might look like. I was convinced that there had to be a way of depicting it. Finally, one morning in 2010, I began to draw something. What emerged was a circular template that was a nondominator model—that is, without the need for a hierarchical organization that codifies "better than" and "less than" relationships between individuals—with multiple applications, including for business, health care, education, organizations, and even individuals as a know-thyself tool. The circular template I drew can be broadly defined as a nondominator or nonhierarchical holistic organizational chart. Since 2010, it seems to have taken on a life of its own, pulling me along a path of healing and development. This book is about that path. The mainstream acceptance of holism in the latter part of the twentieth century nurtured me along the journey. Holism encompasses the circular interrelationship of the physical, mental, emotional, social, and spiritual aspects of life.

One purpose of this book is to increase the understanding and practical application of the circular paradigm. I've included clinical stories alongside personal stories in an attempt to do this. Sample applications of the circular template are featured in some chapters. Suggestions for applications are given in other chapters. If you want to apply these suggestions visually, there is a blank worksheet at the end of the book you may reproduce. In my experience so far, the smallest workable size for the forms is eleven by seventeen inch paper. If you find the circular template too difficult to apply to a particular situation, consider studying the linear and circular characteristics. That process alone can provide significant insights and foster growth and learning, as well as move you toward integrating the characteristics of the circular.

This introduction and each chapter feature specific holistic philosophy concepts. Those that may be less familiar are explained. Because holism includes the circular interrelationship of the physical, mental, emotional, social, and spiritual aspects of life, this book will include information and resources for partnering the knowledge of the head with the wisdom and intelligence of the physical body, emotions, and spirit. The hierarchical box model focuses on the knowledge of the head. Now, with a nonhierarchical model, we begin relying on the wisdom and intelligence of the body, emotions, and spirit. You will be given an opportunity to practice this at the end of each chapter by applying the Hebrew idea of *selah*, which means "stop and listen" or "pause and think of that." Each chapter ends with an invitation for you to practice *selah* by reflecting on what that chapter can help you learn in connection with the quiet, but powerful, intelligence and wisdom of your body, emotions, and spirit.

At the end of each chapter, space has been provided for you to record your responses and notes. I invite you to write about the provided study question and/or whatever occurs to you in the *selah* time. One form of writing I encountered particularly helped me get in touch with the intelligence and wisdom of my body, emotions, and spirit. You may want to consider experimenting with it as part of your exploration of the ideas in this book. The task is to write a question with your dominant hand. Then place the pencil or pen in your nondominant hand and answer your question (Capacchione, 14–5). The process is slow, and it helped me articulate thoughts and access unconscious information I didn't know I could access. Another approach is to focus on your heart, gut, and head responses using the chart provided. The structured thinking may challenge you to record and then move beyond your head responses, which for most of us are familiar and therefore comfortable. You may want to organize a *selah* sharing circle that meets face to face or electronically. Sharing circles can be a meaningful venue in which to share what came up for you about your life as a result of this study.

The ultimate challenge is making holism visible while dancing with a hierarchy that has been entrenched for centuries. Therefore, the most important part of the book is examining how to visually merge the hierarchical and the nonhierarchical, the linear and the circular, in a healthier manner, helping to literally and figuratively increase a sense of partnership.

This book is meant to be educational, contemplative, and reflective. Your truth lies within you. I hope you find this volume helpful. If it isn't, then that can also be helpful, because you will have come closer to clarifying which approaches work for you and which do not. How you resonate with ideas matters. In fact, resonance is one of the central concepts of a holistic philosophy. Resonance could be understood as a vibrating quality between two entities. In resonance, we dance *with* someone rather than occupy either a controlling or dominated role. The following clinical story illustrates resonance. The names in the clinical stories (and some of the personal stories) have been changed to protect the privacy of each person.

CAR DANCES

To cope with the advancing symptoms of Alzheimer's disease, Eve had moved to assisted living from a senior independent apartment. Two of her great pleasures in life had been dancing and driving. She described trips where she drove and her husband sat in the passenger seat and worked or read. They regularly spent evenings at a local ballroom, dancing the night away. After he died, she was lonely. Eve needed some outings that didn't require the complexity of socializing, in addition to needing a health-care advocate, so I was called in. Our outings gave us an opportunity to incrementally build a trusting relationship, a definite need for someone with no children and no family in the area. Partially because of her "aloneness," Alzheimer's understandably brought on some paranoid tendencies. This provided specific challenges in building a trusting relationship. As a strategy to help us overcome those challenges, our shared outings had therapeutic value.

It was not easy to find outings that were meaningful to Eve. When she walked with a walker, and could no longer drive, how could I connect through dancing or driving? One day we drove past a huge empty church parking lot. I pulled into the parking lot, put a tape in the tape deck, and turned up the music that she and her husband had danced to in their youth, the big band sounds of World War II. I invited her to put both hands over onto the steering wheel. I told her we were going to dance the car. She rhythmically and slowly turned the steering wheel, closed her eyes, and allowed a huge smile to slowly spread across her face. She (we) danced the car safely in this huge empty parking lot. When she eventually opened her eyes and released the steering wheel, she was visibly relaxed and happy. This became a favorite outing, promoting connection and relaxation, practicing presence, and dancing with resonance.

❈ ❈ ❈

Selah:

stop and listen.

Study question: In what ways have you let go of dominating and controlling to figuratively "dance with"?

HEART RESPONSES	GUT RESPONSES	HEAD RESPONSES

1

Hide and Seek

Holistic philosophy concept featured: the felt sense

I hid in the closet. It was safer that way. I had discovered that I didn't practice nursing solely with head knowledge the way most other nurses did. More innate and intuitive kinds of knowing from my gut and heart entered into my practice as well. Though I adhered to legal standards, I focused on establishing a relationship with the client as the core of whatever intervention would be needed to give nursing care. To build that core relationship, I tried to keep one foot in the client's world and one foot in my world. This could be further described as keeping the left brain in the scientific knowledge world and the right brain, heart, and gut in the client's world. Tapping into information from "body intelligence"—from the heart and gut, from those other wise organs below the neck—has been crucial for my interventions to succeed. This meant being truly present with clients wherever they were at the time. It meant joining and connecting with them responsibly in their world, as well as endeavoring to bring to them whatever head knowledge would help in their current state of being.

Occasionally, I would quietly and anonymously share a client story with a colleague or two. Finally, nursing professor Dr. Ellen Schultz, murmured softly that she thought I would resonate with Dr. Helen Erickson's holistic nursing theory of modeling and role-modeling. I was leery, because I had never found nursing theories helpful. They seemed impractical, too heady and theoretical, and reliant on an unrealistic, perfect world. Theories were for educators. But I opened myself to the notion of exploring Erickson's theory since I held Professor Schultz's quiet, caring wisdom in high esteem.

During my ensuing explorations, I found the following definition of the central tenets of Erickson's theory:

> *Modeling* is the process by which the nurse seeks to understand her client's unique model of the world. *Role-modeling* is the process by which the nurse understands that unique model within the context of scientific theories and, using that same perspective of her client's unique model, plans interventions that promote health. (Erickson, Tomlin, and Swain, 97)

I felt vindicated and affirmed. After forty-five years in nursing, I was released from a need to hide how I practiced. Here was a formal theory that described and validated what was working in my own practice of nursing. It was the first theory that felt based in the real world for me. My heart overflowed with gratitude then, and still does today.

In the caring professions, much has been taught about the development of listening skills. Effective listening conveys that the nurse wants to listen, that he or she is totally present. Clients more readily trust the nurse who shows a desire to listen and the ability to be present. As a result, clients are more likely to share the model of their world at a deeper and more effective level because the nurse has connected with them and started the foundation of a partnership-based relationship.

Effective listening also includes listening from the heart, with body intelligence. There is much intelligence below the neck and in our instinctual and intuitive responses, or felt senses, that can guide us in our interventions. Eugene Gendlin writes:

> A felt sense is not a mental experience but a physical one. Physical. A bodily awareness of a situation or person or event. An internal aura that encompasses everything you feel and know about the given subject at a given time—encompasses it and communicates it to you all at once rather than detail by detail. (32)

Peter Levine weighs in on the topic with, "Perhaps the best way to describe the felt sense is to say that it is the experience of being in a living body that understands the nuances of its environment by way of its responses to that environment" (69). He goes on to say, "Nowadays the phrase, 'trust your gut' is used commonly. The felt sense is the means through which you can learn to hear this instinctual voice" (72).

Because the felt sense is a foreign concept in our heady culture, it may help to look at two practical applications. The first example is from the clinical world. The second example is a personal life story.

YOU'LL NEVER CRAWL ALONE

Tess lived in a care suite at a local senior building. She had Parkinson's disease and restless leg syndrome. Sometimes the only relief she was able to get from her restless legs was to walk up and down the hall in her walker. Her Parkinson's progressed to the point that she was rarely able to use her walker. She was primarily in her wheelchair. Her restless legs got worse, and one week her face was more pained than I had ever seen it. The maximum ordered medication dose had been used, and rubbing her legs was not helping as it sometimes had. Breathing deeply didn't help. We tried distraction by going for a wheelchair ride outside, and had to abort this due to her leg discomfort. She asked that we stop at the fountain on the way back from the ride. She found the sound comforting. She also said she felt like chewing when her legs started to get restless, so I offered to get her some chewing gum.

I talked with her about getting more medication, which would make her pretty foggy. She opted to be foggy rather than live as she was. I offered to get a tabletop fountain that she could keep beside her bed, and she brightened at the prospect. She thought that would be a "great thing to be foggy to." When I returned later in the day with a fountain and some chewing gum for her, she was in the living room of her suite, waiting at the table for her dinner. She was obviously miserable. She said crawling on the floor sometimes helped in the past and asked if she could get down on the floor until her dinner came. I lowered her to the floor and she began to crawl. My heart hurt for her: such a dignified lady crawling alone on the floor. I couldn't walk away. What could I do?

My body remembered something my mind had forgotten. It was 1967 and as a student nurse, I was doing my psych rotation in a state hospital. My patient had Huntington's chorea, a degenerative hereditary disorder that causes quick, involuntary movements, speech difficulties, and mental deterioration. No one could get close to her or communicate with her. When I tried, she turned and walked stiffly away. I kept following her. Finally, to escape me, she went into the ward's clothing room and sat under a rack of clothing. I went and sat under the rack of clothing with her. That did it: she began to talk with me and welcomed me into her life.

This body memory brought me to my knees on the floor with Tess and we crawled together. She was not alone in her pain. She never looked over at me or spoke to me. She stopped at one point on all fours. She reached her nearest "step" hand over and put it gently on top of my hand. I turned my hand over so we were holding hands. We stayed that way for a few moments, and then we were off again, crawling together in her discomfort. She was not alone. Joining her where she was and my engaged presence were all I could offer her, and it was enough.

A WISE FOOT

I was halfway home. The hail started, and I could see the hailstones were getting bigger and bigger. I knew car damage was a given at that point. I saw two trees ahead and pulled under one to get some protection from the canopy. Another driver had pulled under the first tree. I listened to the hail on my car roof and watched it on hers. I could tell she was getting more protection than I was. I looked up and saw the canopy of her tree was much bigger than the tree I was under. There were about two car lengths between us. I decided I should pull up and get more of the protection under the larger canopy of her tree.

I just sat there. My foot would not leave the brake. I couldn't figure out why I wasn't pulling forward. I questioned myself several times. Within about sixty seconds, her tree came down, and the huge trunk landed at a perfect angle right between our cars. If I had pulled forward, I would have been crushed. As it was, I simply got hit by the tips of the small branches at the top of the tree. The hood of my car was somewhat damaged by the branches in addition to the hail damage to the paint. Sometimes the body is wiser than the head.

❀ ❀ ❀

Selah:

stop and listen.

Study question: Keeping partnership in mind, how do these words from Jewish philosopher Martin Buber (1878–1965) relate to the felt sense: "Only as the You becomes present does presence come into being" (63)?

HEART RESPONSES	GUT RESPONSES	HEAD RESPONSES

2

Two Paradigms

Holistic philosophy concepts featured: relationship, presence, connecting, and sharing information

At this moment in history, we rely on our head intelligence and a linear-thinking paradigm, about 90 percent of the time. The circular paradigm, which allows us to access the wisdom and intelligence of the body, we might use 10 percent of the time, if that. Let's look at some characteristics of these two paradigms (see table 1).

Table 1. Paradigm Characteristics

CHARACTERISTICS	CURRENT LINEAR PARADIGM	EMERGING CIRCULAR PARADIGM
Relationship style	Inferior/superior; ranking; confrontation	Equality; linking; affiliation
Results	Competition; comparison	Contribution; cooperation; collaboration

CHARACTERISTICS	CURRENT LINEAR PARADIGM	EMERGING CIRCULAR PARADIGM
Focus/brain/energy	External/left/electrical	Internal/right/magnetic
Purpose	Defend; protect	Learn
Power	Power over; dominate	Power with, within; actualize
Orientation	Product; "doing"; task	Process; "being"; relate
Motivation	Fear	Love
Plane	Vertical	Horizontal
Conflict	Win/lose or lose/lose Forgiveness as an act	Win/win Forgiveness as an attitude
Modus operandi	Over- or under-responsible; blaming; shaming; magic bullets; quick fixes; avoiding; do it all myself; suppressing	Self-responsible; accountable; self-directed; accepting; ask for help; expressive
Nature's example	Sun: direct, clear, linear rays	Moon: deep, dark, mysterious cycles
Emphasis	Dependence, independence, money	Interdependence, mutuality, synergy

After the events of September 11, 2001, I observed our society reverse the 90/10 percentages for about two weeks. As a group we became more circular, focused on cooperation, and collaborative—and less competitive, in part because we shared a common threat. Then as the freshness of the memories faded, we reverted to our familiar competitive, confrontational, and linear way of life. We frantically race from one thing to the next, desperate to be on top of our schedules and to control other people. After all, if the only two options are superiority or inferiority, the discomfort of being below will drive us to try to be on top. Thus, there is constant jockeying for position. We get addicted to the adrenaline high of risk-taking and winning. This would account for our collective frantic, health-threatening, high-stress lifestyle, which has lasting implications in our unsustainable health-care system. Most of our unresolved health issues today are from stress. When under stress, our adrenaline surges. If adrenal (adrenaline) burnout increases to epidemic proportions, our society won't be able to respond for survival in emergencies, as our bodies were designed to do. Is that where we're headed?

There are times when the head approach of the left brain is needed, and other times that experiential right brain and body intelligence approaches are needed. Until we understand and are able to access both options, we have no choice. In a culture that cherishes the linear options, the circular model is largely unknown and is, at best, ignored.

There has long been a visual for illustrating the linear paradigm. The focus is on organizing people and the lines of communication in top-down hierarchies (see figure 1).

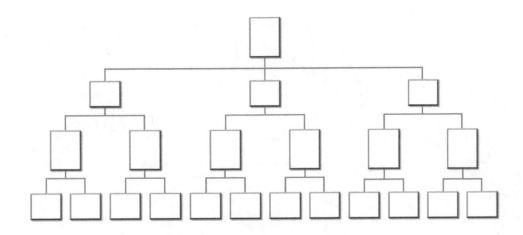

Figure 1. Traditional linear template.

In figure 1, the energy flows vertically and the characteristics of the linear paradigm in table 1 are supported. These characteristics are present in all aspects of our lives: social, political, and religious realms, and in the educational, organizational, and business worlds. The linear model emphasizes dependence for most, independence for some, and money from all. When energy is limited to the vertical flow of the linear paradigm, energy flow is blocked in other directions.

Visuals are powerful. We are influenced by them consciously and unconsciously. The modern world has not had a visual that illustrates or supports the characteristics of the circular paradigm. Perhaps this contributes to the overwhelming focus on the linear paradigm. This may also contribute to the challenge of understanding, supporting, and living out the characteristics of the circular paradigm. Relationship, presence, connecting, and sharing information are concepts emphasized by holistic nursing and in *The 3rd Alternative,* a book by internationally respected authority on leadership Stephen Covey (particularly on pages 180 through 186 in that volume). An increasing number of sources—Covey's book and a volume by corporate executive and management consultant Keshavan Nair, *A Higher Standard of Leadership: Lessons from the Life of Gandhi,* and many holistic nursing articles and texts—make use of circular illustrations. *Circular* connects to the notion of circulation, which in turn relates to the job of the heart. Again, there are health implications. When we deny circular flow, we block our heart energy, and these blocks could well manifest physically as heart disease. In more ways than one, we need to internalize a circular paradigm. Therefore, figure 2 is presented as an option for that visual.

Figure 2. The circular template.

Circular illustrations are more complex than linear ones, because the energy flow provides more options and is more interrelated. The emphasis in the circular model is on interdependence, mutuality, and synergy. Circular energy is self-enhancing and sustaining. Notice how energy can flow in at multiple points, and flow from inside out, outside in, and throughout this model. Each layer or ring enhances and thus sustains the energy flow. In contrast, linear energy, as in the flow of electricity, needs relay stations or transformers to maintain the energy level. Constantly playing those roles can be exhausting.

Two examples follow that illustrate how the characteristics of this self-enhancing energy flow—with its focus on relationship, presence, connecting, and sharing information—look in a clinical situation and a personal life story.

"OUR FATHER" AS BOUNCER

On occasion, I would volunteer to relieve caregivers and work a twenty-four-hour shift with Kay. Her bedtime routine was to read from her daily church reading booklet, after which we would say the "Our Father" prayer together, sitting on the side of her bed. At first, we bowed our heads and closed our eyes. Later on, as her Alzheimer's progressed, I noticed her words were not always in sync with mine. She was forgetting the words and had her eyes open, watching my mouth. By then, we had known each other longer and had established a tradition of holding hands as we prayed. We started saying the prayer looking directly into each other's eyes. For those of us who work with Alzheimer's patients, it is often evident that it is a disease of regression back into a more childlike state. As Kay regressed, she recited the "Our Father" prayer in a cadence that had her moving our hands to that rhythm, applying vocal emphasis at each downward movement of our clasped hands. I always let her lead in that. She needed to have some aspect of life where she felt some control.

As the disease progressed, the hand movements increased in size. One night she began including a bit of a push on the floor with her feet as we started the upward movement of our hands. My body intelligence and memory clicked in. I didn't realize it until it was over. I joined her in the push on the floor so we were bouncing on the bed, just as children like to do, but we were sitting. By the time we were saying "amen," we had worked up quite a rhythm as we bounced and said it over and over, louder and louder, bouncing (carefully) higher and higher until she leaned back, laughing and laughing, maintaining tension in our arms, and then coming forward and wrapping her arms around me. We connected in joyful, childlike adoration of the Sacred Heart.

GIFTS FROM UNCONSCIOUS LESSONS

Mom always had an ability to use the instinctual, the innate, and the felt sense—all are aspects of intuition. Hummingbirds nested in her fuchsia plant outside the east kitchen window, likely because there was a hummingbird feeder a few feet away. Mom spent most of her kitchen time at the north window, near the sink, stove, and refrigerator. The hummingbirds figured out that she was the source refilling the feeder and when the feeder became empty, they would fly back and forth multiple times at the north window. Then Mom knew to check and fill their feeder.

Mom's very dear friend Edith was dying of brain cancer. Mom had been trying to get bluebirds in her backyard birdhouse for five years. She'd had no luck despite her persistent attempts. Edith told Mom that when she died, she would send her bluebirds. Edith passed in the late winter, and that spring Mom got bluebirds for the first time.

It is now thirty-five years later. I planned to visit my mom for her ninety-eighth birthday in Indiana. I wanted to share with her some of my heart-centered stories from the forty-five-year nursing career from which I was retiring. I read some of them to her, and she was deeply touched, wondering how I learned to intervene with my clients in such a way. I told her she had taught me and I didn't think she was probably even conscious of it. She was surprised and wondered how she had taught me.

I reminded her of an example from Edith's final months. She had spent time reading to Edith after she could no longer read due to the brain cancer. At one reading, Edith suddenly sat up in bed, anxiously interrupted Mom, and said, "Liz! There are worms crawling out of that book!"

Mom asked, "Where?"

Edith pointed, "Across the top!"

Mom took her hand and scooped across the top of the book. "Did I get them all?" she asked Edith. Edith visibly relaxed back into her pillow and told Mom she had indeed taken care of all the worms. Mom then continued to read to Edith.

I explained to Mom that what she had modeled with that example was how to step into another person's reality and intervene where he or she is. She nodded slowly, saying it was just something she did innately without being aware of it. I then related it to how I had done that in the career stories I had read to her. I thanked her for that gift, letting her know that I'd only become conscious of it after some of my colleagues asked me to write down some of the stories I'd told them over the years.

This was a gift exchange. The first gift, the opportunity to observe and absorb my mother's intuition in action, was given unconsciously. The return gift was to bring consciousness to the action, express gratitude for the modeling of presence and connecting, and acknowledge the positive effect on those who benefitted from this teaching. The most profound legacy, though, was a strengthened relationship between mother and daughter.

❀❀❀

Selah:

stop and listen.

YOUR RESPONSES AND NOTES

Study question: How does presence unconsciously lead us and connect us?

HEART RESPONSES	GUT RESPONSES	HEAD RESPONSES

3

The Emerging Circular Paradigm

Holistic philosophy concept featured: mutuality, i.e., all being equal in our oneness, connectivity, and shared similarities or differences

First, let's look at the physical structure of the circular template (figure 3) and how it can be used. It is a multiple application model that can organize information of all kinds, not only people and company communication structures. The model can be applied in numerous ways for individuals, businesses, and community organizations—and in health care, education, and parenting. It's also useful with a variety of clients.

The template features four rings and a center:

Ring 1: Outer rainbow ring—seven sources or resources

Ring 2: Teaching and learning ring—what each source or resource teaches or contributes

Ring 3: Inner resources ring—resources available from or applied to the body, mind, and spirit (ancient cultures included emotions in the mind arena)

Ring 4 and center: Manifestation ring—based on the fêng shui ba-gua system and its life aspects.

Figure 3. Generic details of the circular template.

Besides the Chinese influence of the fêng shui *ba-gua* system, the template connects to the Hindu and Tibetan gift of the mandala and the European tradition of labyrinths. Thus, this template is global in nature. Some definitions may help make sense of these concepts.

Mandala has two definitions according to the dictionary. One is for the individual, the microcosm, and the other is for the cosmos, the macrocosm. The eminent psychiatrist C. G. Jung (1875–1961) spoke to the microcosm definition when he defined the mandala as "a symbol representing the effort to reunify the self" (as cited in *Webster's*). An Asian definition would speak to the macrocosm or cosmos as "a schematized representation of the cosmos characterized by a concentric organization of geometric shapes, each of which contains an image of a deity or an attribute of a deity" (*Webster's*, 870). For our purposes, deity will be considered the seven resources or sources in the outer rainbow ring. Another understanding of the mandala comes from the Sanskrit root word for mandala. That root word means "encircling the essence." In their book on the topic, José and Miriam Argüelles describe that "a Mandala consists of a series of concentric forms, suggestive of a passage between different dimensions" (12). Thus, this template incorporates concepts of unifying, encircling the essence of the applied topic, and creating bridges or passages.

The labyrinth is a path that is walked as a meditative practice. It is not a maze. There is a definitive path in, a center, and a path out. The journey in can be used to release distractions and thoughts, ask questions, and observe awarenesses. The center is a place to stop and wait and receive, letting in the lessons and the presence of the center. The journey out is an opportunity to integrate the lessons and awarenesses, gradually returning to reality. Labyrinths are often found at sacred sites. Typical labyrinths have one entry and a clear path to the center and then to one exit point. For the template, a multientry labyrinth variation is used. This means a person can mentally enter wherever they are drawn, and explore the areas about which they are curious in whatever order they choose. This characteristic of the model draws from the basic principle that one learns best when motivated from within.

The fêng shui *ba-gua* is a Chinese way of studying the relationship between the environment, energy flow, harmony, and success. It is a map or visual tool that can be applied to any space. It consists of nine *guas*, or life aspects, in a particular configuration, with each life aspect assigned its own color:

1. Fame/reputation (red)
2. Partnerships/relationships (pink)
3. Creativity/children/communication (white)
4. Helpful people/benefactors (gray)
5. Career/path (black)
6. Knowledge (blue)
7. Family/community (green)
8. Wealth (purple)
9. Health/balance in the center (yellow)

In the template, we use these life aspects to become more conscious of how and what we are manifesting or want to manifest.

The circular has been suppressed by the emphasis on the perceived superiority of the linear approach. This suppression has wounded both the circular and linear participants. Neither can be authentic or trusting. The circular participants feel a need to hide and feel less-than, and the linear participants are weighed down by excess responsibility and expectations of perfection. Equality can be increased by integrating the circular model. This means aiming for experiences of mutuality. Mutuality includes reciprocity, mutual enhancement, community, balance, integration, completeness, oneness, and wholeness. We are all messy mortals, so we won't achieve these experiences constantly; however, aiming for them brings more positive energy into our world.

The stories that follow illustrate what mutuality experiences look like clinically and in a personal life story.

A LESSON IN PRIDE

The facility called me one very hot day in the summer. The temperature was in the mid-nineties. My Alzheimer's client, Eve, had soiled herself and was refusing to change clothes. She was sitting in the lounge and was soiling furniture and causing others to leave the room. Could I come and see what I could do? When I arrived, Eve smiled and we went to her room. I had on sandals and summer clothing for a hot day. Eve had dressed herself in wool for the day. I asked her if she would like to go out for an ice cream cone, and she was excited. I noted how I was dressed and how hot it was out, and maybe she wanted to change into something cooler. She agreed. As I helped her undress, I found stool even down in her shoes. I noted we had to clean her up a bit before putting on cooler clothing. Big mistake! She angrily stamped out into the lounge and refused to come back into her room.

I sat and pondered. I had wounded her pride, caused her shame. Now I needed to repair it. I turned on the water in the bathtub and took off my sandals. I put my feet in the water and just sat there. Before too long, curiosity got the best of Eve. She came back into her room and peeked around the corner into the bathroom. As soon as I saw her, I said, "Oh, Eve, thank you so much for letting me use your tub. It is so hot out and my feet were so hot I needed to cool them off." She cocked her head and nodded stiffly, and turned and left. She came back several more times. Each time I said the same thing, and each time she paused at the door a bit longer, smiling bigger each time. When it felt like her pride had been restored, just after she left that time, I quickly got a towel and washcloth from her cupboard and clothes from her closet and brought them to the bathroom. The next time she came, I was ready. This time I told her that thanks to her generosity I had adequately cooled off my feet, so I was ready to go for an ice cream cone now if she wanted to go along. Oh yes, she did, and she was willing to change into cooler clothes. So I distracted her with chatter the entire time I helped her undress, and just began washing her without saying what I was doing or why. After washing, she was ready for the clean clothes that were laid out for her. Off we went! Pride restored in one of us, and an important lesson learned by the other.

BOUNDING BEYOND FEAR

One day I decided to practice my deep-relaxation breathing outdoors, so I headed for my favorite tree in the woods. I breathed rhythmically as I walked through the snow on the one-person path. Far ahead, I saw a woman and dog approaching. The dog stopped as soon as it saw me, went behind the woman, and peeked out at me. I saw her talk with the dog; no luck. Automatically, without thinking, I stopped. My body immediately took one step off the path and knelt down in the snow. I didn't move a muscle. I breathed relaxation to the dog. The dog advanced about six feet. The woman worked with the dog more. I didn't flinch, and continued to breathe relaxation to the dog. The dog continued with this pattern of slow advancing. When the dog got close enough, I slowly put out my hand and talked soothingly. The dog sniffed my hand, came and licked my face, then bounded for joy all around me. When the woman tried to call the dog off, I objected, saying I thought this was incredible. The woman looked at me very perplexed, and with tearful and halting words expressed appreciation for how I had been with her dog. When the dog's experience was so clearly fear and I felt that fear, we had a mutual exchange at the heart level.

☀☀☀

Selah:

stop and listen.

Study question: What are your internal responses when you are approached in the spirit of authority instead of mutuality?

HEART RESPONSES	GUT RESPONSES	HEAD RESPONSES

4

An Exercise in Felt Sense

Holistic philosophy concepts featured: self-care and self-responsibility

Let's pause now to reflect—and practice the felt sense. Look at the two visuals we have explored as the two paradigms (figure 4).

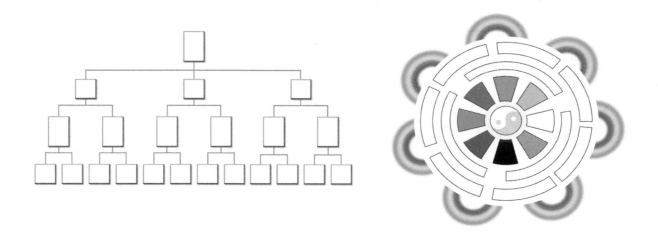

Figure 4. Felt-sensing the templates.

What do you feel? It may help to reflect on good, as well as difficult, experiences you may have had with each paradigm. Just write down whatever comes to you. In the linear model, which of the boxes have you been in? What was your experience of it or them? Did you feel inferior, superior, anxious, threatened, exhausted, challenged, elated, or motivated? Was your adrenaline working overtime? What else? In the circular model, did you feel at sea, chaotic, lost, free, supported, valued, a part of a whole, or a calm energy? What else?

We can dull our feelings in many ways, and most of us are pros at numbing ourselves because we've been taught that feelings aren't acceptable. We overindulge in a variety of substances or behaviors to stop those unwelcome, and perhaps sometimes overwhelming, feelings.

Feelings are a great source of information—and they are all valid. When we reach emotional maturity, we manage our feelings in constructive ways. We take responsibility for our feelings. How can you constructively take responsibility for the feelings that arise for you as you reflect in this exercise? This is all about self-care and self-responsibility. (Chapter 11 will offer more details on self-responsibility.)

Now focus on your body sensations as you look at figure 4. This might be a challenge since we're so indoctrinated to stay in our heads and ignore what we feel, experience, and know below the neck. Do you have a lump in your gut? Do your legs feel heavy? Does your heart ache? Notice your breathing as you sit with each figure. Do your hands or feet feel cold or hot as you do this? Do you feel immobilized when you encounter one of the visuals, but not the other?

Our bodies help us find our truth, and each person's truth is what really matters. Sometimes I wonder if the exhortation in John 8:32, "And you will know the truth, and the truth will set you free" really means "You will know your truth, and your truth will set you free."

Accessing your felt sense is a process. It takes time to access it—and we think we don't have time in our current frantic lifestyles. Don't rush this. Come back to it as you continue to write and read. You are worth it. This can be part of taking responsibility for a self-care practice.

What might self-care practices look like clinically and in everyday life? This example combines both. Part of my self-care practice is to dilute my tendency for being serious and intense with some humor. Note the simplicity of the self-care the client is capable of at this point in her disease, and the lines in the sand I drew as part of my self-care.

BRINGING DOWN THE (OUT) HOUSE

As Eve's dementia intensified, so did her paranoia. She hid anything she perceived to be of value. One day the trust officer asked me to get her to sign some papers. She had hidden her glasses, and all we could find were her sunglasses. She consented to sign the papers, and perched her sunglasses on top of her head while we sat down to the table to sign the papers. I showed her the line on which to sign. She brought her sunglasses down to her eyes, took pen in hand, and was about to sign when she noticed her sleeve was not in the right place. She pushed up her sleeve and we went through the orientation again, where to sign, glasses in place, about to sign, and then the other sleeve was not in the right place. This must have happened four times. Finally, all was in place and she was ready to sign. She brought her sunglasses down to her nose again, and angrily stated, "Geez! It's dark in here!"

Part of my philosophy is that I'm meant to learn from every client I have. Sometimes my lesson is to learn to laugh at myself. Shortly after Eve's paper-signing experience, my friend Sue and I headed off to a cabin in the Wisconsin woods for a weekend getaway. It was remote and rustic, meaning it had no running water or electricity. We swam in the lake, then sat in the wooded yard and talked and talked. At one point, I needed to use the outhouse down the path. Upon reaching the outhouse, I closed the door and immediately realized there was no source of light and I could not see the seat. I opened the door and got a bead on the location of the seat and closed the door again. I turned around and concluded I would have to grope to find the seat, and drew a line in the sand: I wasn't going to grope in an outhouse. I opened the door again, and once more drew a line in the sand. No, I wasn't going to use an outhouse with the door open. I closed the door again, and said out loud, with impatience, "Geez! It's dark in here!" With that, I realized I had my sunglasses on. When I took them off, I could see just fine. I laughed and thanked Eve for helping me solve that problem.

❀ ❀ ❀

Selah:

stop and listen.

YOUR RESPONSES AND NOTES

Study question: How is laughing at yourself part of self-care?

HEART RESPONSES	GUT RESPONSES	HEAD RESPONSES

5

The Circular Paradigm in an Organization

Holistic philosophy concept featured: unconditional respect

The first application of the template we will look at is for an interfaith church, shown in figure 5. Let's look at the rings:

Ring 1: Shows the source or deities for seven of the world's religions.

Ring 2: Shows the prophets and teachers for each of the sources.

Ring 3: Shows the inner resources of the church in the areas of body, mind, and spirit.

Ring 4: Shows the manifestation ring, specifies the committees and programs that speak to each life aspect of the fêng shui ba-gua.

The center, which this church chose to depict as a spiral that includes concepts deemed important for the health and balance of the church, is denoted by the yin-and-yang symbol in the original template.

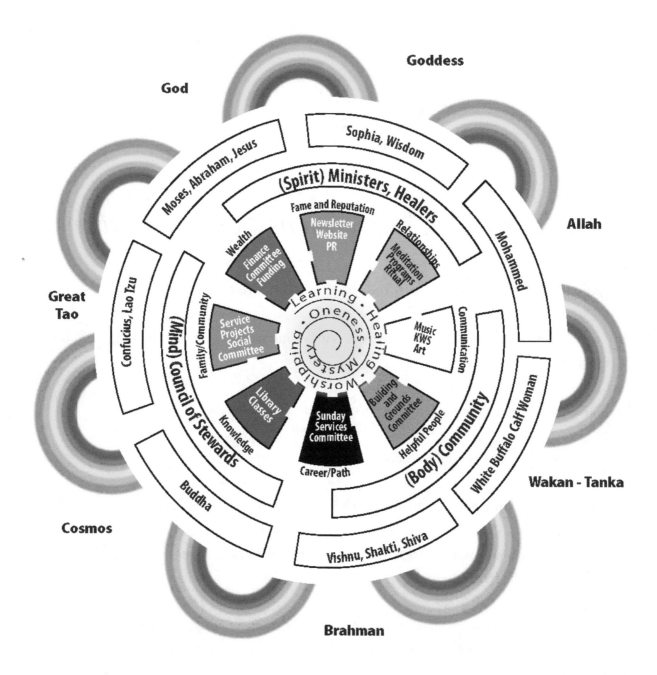

Figure 5. Interfaith church mandala application.

Figure 5 is the organizational chart this church has put in place. There are no vertical lines to block energy. Lines of communication could be shown by arches. Energy passes through arches. For example, each member of the Council of Stewards could be listed and shown to be the communication link for one program or committee with an arch indicating this. The arches and the center spiral give this chart a three-dimensional effect, bringing it into the twenty-first century.

Note that a person could enter this community at any point with which they resonate (multientry labyrinth concept). They are free to wander all around and learn about any other source and its associated teachings. In the process, they'll become acquainted with the inner resources: the community members, the Council of Stewards, and the ministers and healers. When they're ready, they can explore the programs or committees. In each life-aspect program or committee, there is a side-window opening to learn about that program or committee. Once the person decides in what program or committee they want to become involved, they go in the door of that life aspect, which is nearer the center. This suggests deeper involvement with the concepts on the spiral. The exploration brings people to the heart of the organization, instead of bringing them to a box.

Allowing heart entrance and opening is less predictable and riskier than having everything in a neat and tidy box. However, the results yield unconditional respect, as the following clinical and everyday life examples depict.

HEART ALTARS

Peter was an eighteen-year-old man in a ten-year-old's body with a six-month-old's brain. He was hit by a car as he crossed the street and was taken to a hospital. Due to a medical error, he suffered an anoxic period that left him in his current state of being. His parents had cared for him round the clock since the accident. He hadn't suffered any skin breakdown, and had outlived the life expectancy provided for in the legal settlement following the medical error. When I was asked to take his case, I was told the family had terminated every other nurse that had been hired, so I shouldn't take it personally if the assignment didn't work out.

On my first visit, Peter's older brother answered the door, and acted as the interpreter for the immigrant family. I noticed all the shoes at the entry, and immediately sat down on the step to take off my shoes. There was lots of chatter behind me—the extended family had many children. When I turned to get up on one knee, a ring of shining preschool eyes was watching me. One little girl ran over and sat on my knee. Another little boy came and stood right next to me. I put my arm around both, and we visited a bit. I was being watched by the adults, intently. Soon the little boy ran off, but the little girl remained wrapped around me. I stood up. I had noticed string around some twigs at the ceiling level, crossing the dining area, and disappearing around the corner into the living room. As I walked and talked with the little girl in my arms, I began to follow the twig path. I saw it ended at an altar on the outside wall of the living room. I turned and asked if we could go to the altar. I was given permission with a nod, and the instruction "just don't touch." I approached the altar, standing back far enough to make it obvious that neither the child nor I could touch anything. When she wanted down, I put my hands behind my back. After honoring the altar, I turned and asked if I could now see Peter. The parents nodded and we went into the bedroom. I talked with Peter, even though he couldn't respond verbally. His parents showed me all the cupboards, supplies, and everything they used in Peter's care. I was grateful that I was accepted at this point.

I expressed interest in a fishing net that was being woven over a curtain rod in the bedroom. They told me, with great pride, how this was done in their home country. When it was finished, the net would be sent as a gift to relatives back in their home country. The family's heart was still there. I felt respect for their pride in their humble culture.

TAKING RISKS

I was taught early in life that it was a sin to dance. My parents' generation and religion were the source of this belief. I was able to remove those shackles at age fifty-two, and I began a variety of types of dance lessons. I settled on interpretive dance as my chosen expression.

When visiting my parents in their church-affiliated retirement center five years later, I happened upon a trio singing hymns to a group of residents in my dad's nursing home. Mom and Dad were in the front row (as usual) of two semicircular rows of wheelchairs around the trio and piano. By then Mom and Dad knew I was dancing, and although they didn't object, Mom was always worried about what others would think. I was at the back of the group and began to move to the music. When the hymn ended, the trio motioned to me to "come into the middle and do that," so I moved into the middle of the semicircle.

Mom has always been a singer, doing solos and participating in quartets and choirs all her life. She always sings with her head held high; she told me that's how singers can best project their voices. After I moved to the center and began moving to the next song, I looked over at my mom. She was singing with her head down, looking at the floor.

After the song, cheers and applause and compliments were thrown my way during the visiting that always happened between songs. This happened after each successive song and I noticed Mom's head came up a notch after each one. Finally, toward the end, she was singing with her head held high again. When one woman engaged her in conversation before the last song, Mom interrupted her, pointed at me, and said, "That's my daughter, you know!"

About midway through all the singing, a woman with a facility-issued name tag came down the hall and stopped at the corner, arms folded, and watched. At the end of the singing, she made a beeline for me. I was wary. When she was just a few steps from me, she stretched out her arms and I saw her eyes were welled up with tears. She complimented me while embracing me, thanked me profusely, and then rushed away. A number of other staff talked with me about what I had done.

As I walked with my mom back to her apartment, she asked me what the chaplain said to me. I told her I didn't know the chaplain. She described the woman who had been standing at the corner, and then came and hugged me. I told Mom that she'd complimented me and expressed her gratitude. Mom seemed dumbfounded. "Really?" she asked.

We were quiet until we got to her sofa, where I sat down next to her. "Mom, when you and Dad were younger, did you take risks in the church?" I asked her.

She was emphatic with her positive response.

I continued, "If I took the same risks as you took, they wouldn't be risks anymore now, would they?" She readily agreed. Only one question remained, "Mom, can you let me take the risks that are mine to take?"

Long silence. "Yes, I guess I can," she replied.

Each time I remember Mom's "That's my daughter, you know!" between hymns, my heart and eyes fill up. I had waited fifty-seven years to hear that. It was well worth the risk of stepping into that semicircle to earn the respect.

❀ ❀ ❀

Selah:

stop and listen.

YOUR RESPONSES AND NOTES

Study question: What influences your intention to be respectful?

HEART RESPONSES	GUT RESPONSES	HEAD RESPONSES

6

The Circular Paradigm in Nursing Education

Holistic philosophy concepts featured: trust and collaboration

The holistic nursing mandala illustrates how the circular paradigm applies to nursing. This specialized mandala (figure 6) places the seven major holistic nurse theorists—Barbara Dossey, Helen Erickson, Margaret Newman, Florence Nightingale, Rosemarie Parse, Martha Rogers, and Jean Watson—on the outer ring as sources, or resources. The second ring lists the titles of their theories. The third ring includes the inner resources of the American Holistic Nurses Association (AHNA), the national professional organization. The fourth ring shows a few samples of information based on the use assigned to that ring. Figure 7 gives more detail of the third and fourth rings due to the concentration of information in those rings. AHNA's core values occupy the body area (past) of the third ring; the mission statement sits in the mind area (present); and the vision statement resides in the spirit area (future). The holistic concepts from all of the theories are shown in the fourth, or manifestation, ring (which includes the center), in the life aspect to which they apply. Some concepts could apply to more than one life aspect.

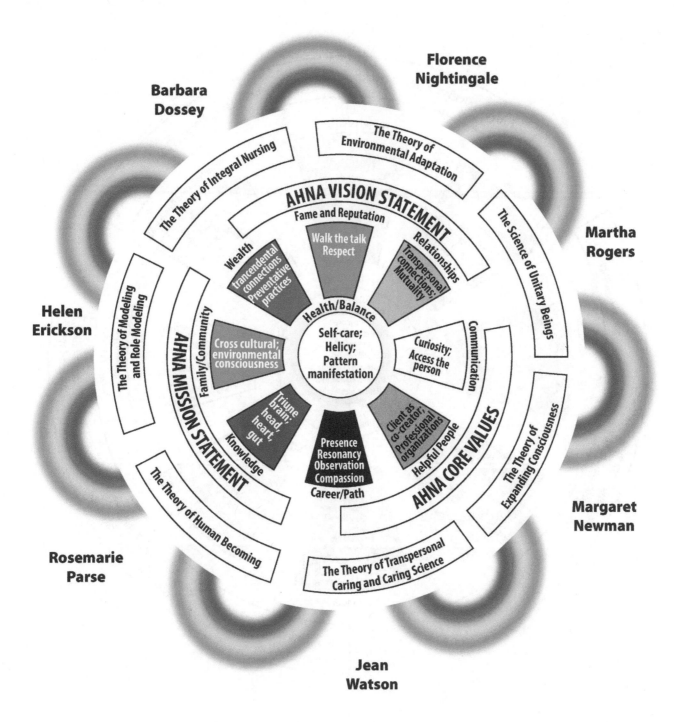

Figure 6. Holistic nursing mandala application—the American Holistic Nurses Association (AHNA).

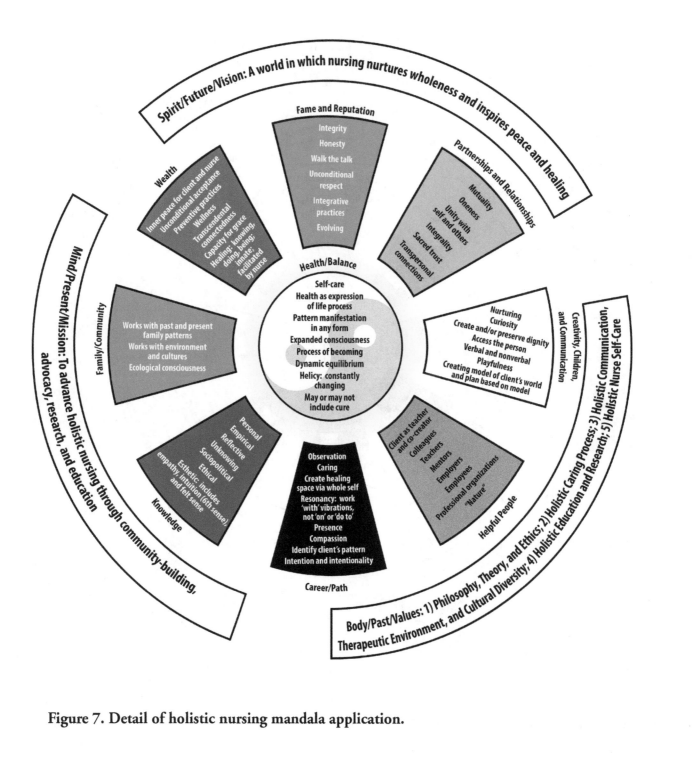

Figure 7. Detail of holistic nursing mandala application.

A useful digital version of figure 6 might allow a click on each theorist that would provide a pop-up window with her biography. Similarly, a click on each theory could provide a pop-up of the theory. The national organization information could be available by clicking on any area of the third ring. In the manifestation ring, information about each concept, which theorists wrote about them and in what context, could be the result of clicking on the given concept. This mandala could become an entire semester's course content on holistic nursing theory. Any other course could be adapted to this format, as well.

The holistic nursing mandala is a good illustration of how this template "encloses the essence" of a topic. Notice that there are multiple entry points allowing for a self-directed journey. This feature can contribute to self-knowledge if you are introspective. You get to observe what calls to you the most, what draws you into the journey, the ideas that resonate for you. Self-knowledge helps bring clarity to what each of us has to offer. With clarity, trust increases, promoting healthier collaboration with clients and other professionals.

The following examples show the benefit of the trust and collaboration concepts. The first is from the clinical world and the second is an illustration from my personal life.

OPPORTUNITY KNOCKS

Kay was an eighty-five-year-old woman who lived in a downtown area. She had no children. She had lived alone since 1984 when her husband died. She was a college graduate, and had a busy schedule supporting her alma mater and participating in various women's clubs and church activities. She was also an avid lover of the orchestra and the theater. She was managing Alzheimer's. She lived very independently and guarded her independence carefully.

When neighbors in her high-rise condo building met me, they sighed long and loud with relief, expressing gratitude for someone finally being there to help her. I hired coverage for her from about 8:00 a.m. through 10:00 p.m., with 10:00 a.m. until 6:00 p.m. as the only span of hours when she would have constant company. Prior to and after these hours, there were intermittent checks on her. At first she liked the coverage. Then she began to resist it. When the resistance came, I suggested we have a team meeting with Kay, the two caregivers, the two trust officers, and me. I arranged to tape the one-hour meeting and have a transcription typed. These minutes were typed in the format of a script for a play, with each speaker's name in the left column and the content of their contribution in the right column.

This format—i.e., minutes in the form of a script—reinforced two of her life experiences, an interest in the theater and the various secretarial duties she had performed as part of her involvement in women's clubs.

About ten days after the meeting, the caregivers and Kay and I sat down and reviewed the "script." We each read our own parts and soon Kay firmly stated that she would be Ben, the male trust officer. As she read Ben's part and her own part, she would stop and say, "I had forgotten all of this!" As a result of our read-through of the script, she seemed to register more fully the importance of our decisions. She gave more credence because it was in the form of minutes—like a business or club. In fact, we began calling the meeting Kay's Klub. The minutes were in a large three-ring binder labeled "Communication Log and Kay's Klub," which she kept on her kitchen counter. She could review them anytime she chose.

My heart helped me "see" what was important to Kay and what made something credible to her. As we prepared for our second meeting, I suggested to Kay that she review the minutes in preparation for the meeting, and she very earnestly and seriously said she would do that. The caregivers used the minutes to help her remember our decisions and the discussion that led to the decisions. This built Kay's trust in her caregivers, which helped her adjust to a change in her circumstances that would require collaborative, round-the-clock care.

Kay needed major surgery. Postoperatively, home-based rehab with occupational and physical therapy was set up. She had to have help twenty-four hours a day, and the student nurses from her alma mater were eager for work. We suggested to Kay that she could help the students at her alma mater by having them stay overnight with her. She loved that idea, and her acceptance of the coverage was never a problem from then on.

In the long term, significant time and energy can be saved when you start by making the effort to establish an effective trust relationship. The following everyday life example is what led to the development of the holistic nursing mandala.

COLLABORATION ACROSS THE VEIL

For fifteen years I tried. Again and again I tried. I held a deep conviction that there could be a nonhierarchical organizational chart. I kept trying to draw one, to no avail. Finally, one January morning in 2010, I got out of bed and just started drawing. I had no plan. The shapes just seemed to ooze from the pencil.

It seemed as if some other force was at work. When the figure was complete, I looked at it and asked myself what this was. I could see a multientry labyrinth. I took it to a group and asked them what they saw. One person said it was a mandala. I kept talking with others and getting their input. After nine months' gestation, it was applied as an organizational chart for a small, interfaith church.

After that, though, I hit many brick walls in attempting to apply it to other situations. By the spring of 2012, I was ready to give up. On April 28, 2012, at 1:30 a.m., I turned over in bed and was about to go back to sleep, when I heard my dad call my name. He'd gone to the other side on March 15, 2008. I replied, "Well, hi, Dad."

He stated very clearly, "I'm sorry, I didn't understand."

"I know you didn't, Dad," I responded. "That's okay."

"How can I help now?" he asked.

I explained that I had this project I felt passionately about, and I was hitting brick walls. I mentioned that he'd been a businessman, and if he had any ideas, I'd like to hear them. With that, his energy seemed to leave the space. I laid there, a bit weepy at the healing exchange. After about ten minutes, he came back. This time I could see his face—it was within what appeared to be the kind of swirl that's often used to depict the Milky Way galaxy.

"Try your professional organization," he told me. Then his face and voice faded away slowly.

I took his advice. When my professional organization initially didn't respond, I became discouraged again. I kept reminding myself that Dad responded to my request for help and I wanted to honor that. Then I received another sign, this one in the form of a saying I encountered in a book of inspirational quotes. The gist of it was that if you are passionate about something, you should do it—whether or not success is assured. In other words, remain true to yourself. I remembered that my dad always said, "Look at what you can do, not at what you can't do." I learned to trust in and collaborate with myself and my passion for this enterprise.

After that turning point, I started doing the project for myself. At one point I had summarized seven of the major holistic nursing theories, and wanted someone to check my summaries and how I applied them to the mandala. I asked my colleague, nursing professor Ellen Schultz, if she'd be willing to check my work, and she readily agreed.

We sat side by side and her fingers skimmed the pages as she nodded and quietly confirmed that my summaries were accurate and my proposed applications of the mandala were understandable. Then, still looking at the pages, she asked, "Would you like to do a poster presentation of this at the upcoming national conference for the Society for the Advancement of Modeling and Role-Modeling?"

I replied that the deadline for that application had already passed, so it wasn't possible.

"I can take care of that," she replied. Unbeknownst to me, she was in charge of the conference.

At the conference presentation, Helen Erickson, who authored the nursing theory of modeling and role-modeling, strongly encouraged me to write a book. And so it is.

❀❀❀

Selah:

stop and listen.

Study question: How do you identify when trust and collaboration messages are communicated to you by your heart and gut, as well as your head?

HEART RESPONSES	GUT RESPONSES	HEAD RESPONSES

7

The Circular Paradigm as a "Know Thyself" Tool

Holistic philosophy concept featured: expanded consciousness

Bill George, former chairman and CEO of Medtronic, Inc. and Harvard professor, wrote a 2011 column in the Minneapolis-based *Star Tribune* stressing the importance of "know thyself." The emerging circular model offers multiple opportunities to foster personal exploration and growth. Here are some ways individuals can apply the circular paradigm in pursuit of increased self-awareness.

One person wanted to list wounds as the seven rainbow ring sources or resources. In ring 2, what could he then learn from each wound, and teach others about what he'd learned? In ring 3, how were his body, mind, and spirit affected by these wounds? And in ring 4 and the center, how was each life aspect affected by the wounds, and what are the resulting goals for each life aspect?

Another person wanted to list skills as the seven rainbow ring sources or resources. In ring 2, how did she learn those skills, and what does she want to teach about those skills? In ring 3, how were her body, mind, and spirit affected by those skills? And in ring 4 and the center, what is working and not working yet in each life aspect, and how could her skills be used to grow in these areas?

To get a life-review perspective, divide your age by seven and use the resulting value to separate your life into seven segments. (So if you're thirty-five, your seven segments will be in five-year increments.) Place one of the seven segments in the space at the end of each rainbow. At the end of the rainbow of each of your seven age segments, note at least one resource or source, such as an influential person(s), experience, animal, book, etc.

For ring 2, what did that person(s), experience, animal, or book teach you? What did you learn from them?

In ring 3, you have several options. One is to describe your body (i.e., size, shape, image), your mind (i.e., learning style, right- or left-brain dominant, your emotional tendencies), and spirit (i.e., spirituality, or think of spirit as energy, like a spirited horse and what energizes you). Another option is to use these three areas to describe your core values (body), your personal mission statement (mind), and your vision statement (spirit) at this point in life.

For ring 4 and the center, how does all this manifest in each life aspect for you? For example, if you noted you are an introvert, then in the fame and reputation life aspect you may prefer to be a behind-the-scenes person. In the relationships or community aspects, you may prefer one on one or small group interactions.

I used the model to explore a question to myself. My question was, "Why is this whole hierarchy topic so important to me?" I divided my life up into seven equal age segments for the rainbow ring spots. In those spots, I added the name(s) of people who embodied the hierarchy to me during that age segment. In ring 2, I noted what I learned from each of them about the hierarchy, pleasant or unpleasant.

In ring 3, I noted what I grew from, then to, for the body, mind, and spirit. This was based on what I had uncovered from age one through the present in the first two rings. In ring 4 and the center, I did the same thing for each life aspect: what I grew from, then what I grew to.

I sat back and studied the completed model, from the beginning to the present. I gasped. It was clear all those experiences with the hierarchy had a purpose. Each expanded on the last one until I arrived at this current project of finding a way to create a visual for a nonhierarchical way of organizing information. I turned a corner and discovered gratitude for all those unpleasant experiences that got me to this rewarding period of my life, instead of regretting them or seeing them as mistakes.

Let's look at an example of what this "know thyself" or expanded consciousness application might look like in a clinical situation. The other example that follows emerged from everyday life.

EASY DOES IT

I called Edna Z. "EZ" because she was usually just that—easy. I could tell before my arrival at her building, though, that this day would be different. My message from the office said she'd called before I was due to be there, to ask why I hadn't arrived yet. Upon my arrival, she was ready to go to the audiologist, and off we went, all ninety-five years and eighty pounds of her.

Her venting started when we got into the car. Her hearing aid was a lemon. No one talked to her or told her anything because she couldn't hear. A man in the building died and she missed his funeral last Friday because no one told her about it. He was a very nice man, a friend. When she went to any events in the building, she couldn't hear anything, so why go? Besides, she knew when to take her medications and how many to take and she didn't know that by answering all those questions the staff asked her, someone would come and take over her medications! She felt cut off. Why was she being told by specialists that there was nothing more they could do for her vision or her hearing? It didn't matter that she finally had a new phone she could use because no one called her anymore, not even her niece.

Part of her hearing-aid problem was a mold, meaning the shape of the device that's inserted into the outer ear, that wouldn't stay seated. When the audiologist offered to fit her with a mold that would stay seated, was softer, and wouldn't hurt her ear as much, she refused because she wasn't guaranteed that she'd be able to get it in and out herself, and she didn't plan to let anyone help her. "I can do it myself, and that is final!" After all, she was only ninety-five, and she planned to "sign on" for five more years.

She did agree to a hybrid ear mold that would be partially softer to help it stay in better, and partially hard, which would thus increase the chances that she'd be able to get it in and out by herself. We all agreed to keep the old mold just in case she could not function independently with the new one.

On the way home, the venting continued. By this time, I'd concluded she really needed to get it all out, so I just listened. When it seemed appropriate, I noted that she sounded discouraged and angry. She agreed. She proceeded to explain more about how cut off she felt. I kept listening until we arrived at her building. As we moved through the lounge, I noticed that anytime we walked together, she kept me on her non-hearing-aid side. As two residents engaged her in conversation, I walked over to the bulletin board and saw the funeral announcement for the upcoming Friday, not the previous Friday. I concluded I needed to stay and talk with her.

We sat down in her kitchen and I told her how I'd noticed two people had engaged her on the way in. I also noted that the funeral in question would be on the upcoming Friday. I asked her if she'd like to go. She firmly stated no, that only if some friend invited her to go along, and even then she'd probably say no. She wouldn't go because she wouldn't be able to hear anything anyway. That's why she never went to meals or activities. I talked with her about where she positioned herself at a table or walking in the hall or in the lounge with regard to her hearing aid. I acknowledged that she may not like what her choices were at age ninety-five, but she did have some choices over some things she could do to make life more pleasant. (For example, she had the impression that she didn't have enough money to run her air conditioner on really hot days, except in the living room. In reality, she had plenty of money to cool the bedroom and bath as well.) She listened, nodded, confessed that she did like her new phone better than the old one—even if her niece never called—and then changed the subject.

We chatted about lighter topics. Soon she wondered if she could get me a soft drink or something. When I declined and said I needed to go soon, she persisted with the thought that surely there was something she could give me. First, I said no, and then I turned back and said, "Well, yes, there is something you can give me." She looked up and a sly grin crossed her face, her eyes began to sparkle, and the familiar low, slow, barely audible chuckle began to rumble. "Oh, I know. A hug," she chortled. With that she stood up as much as her kyphosis—overcurvature of the spine—would let her, took two steps toward me, and embraced me, chuckling all the while. As I walked away, she added the crowning touch. "I think I'll go down and see about signing up for some of those meals." Bingo. Relationship as intervention had worked again! She vented and I listened; I explained and she heard me. I let her save face; she felt respected. Respect from another increased self-respect, and thus self-responsibility. Her consciousness expanded.

A call to the apartment manager netted more cooperation. She would call her once a day so she would get some phone calls, help her sign up for meals, and facilitate her sitting in a "hearing" position when in groups or at meals.

FINDING ESSENCE

I've often said that the universe is weaving a giant tapestry, and we're each a thread with an assigned color and texture. If we aren't true to our individual color and texture, we're messing up the tapestry. At fifty-two, I entered the world of dance as a total foreigner. I had no idea what was involved in this dance world. I didn't know the language or the milieu. When I was introduced to folk dancing in a junior high physical education class, a note was written for me to be excused because it was against my religion. So, I started with folk dancing at fifty-two instead of thirteen. I thought I should start where I left off. After that, I took some ballroom lessons, one tap lesson, and then some ballet lessons. When I told Karen, my ballet teacher, how uncomfortable I was in the leotard, she wondered why. I told her I'd always had a long neck and tried to hide it with a turtleneck or high-necked blouses, and the leotard's low, scooped neckline was the opposite. I thought she was going to have a stroke. "Hide your long neck? Hide your long neck! That's what every dancer wants, is a long neck!" Oh, I didn't know that. I asked for more information about a dancer's body, and learned I had "jumper's legs." That was congruent with my early years when my cousin Dan and I practiced high-jumping together in a high-jump pit he had made down in the field.

My friend Holly, a dancer, was helping me learn about dance as well. I was with her one day and described what I thought was a deficit in my ability to identify rhythms. I noted that when music came on, I had to find the beat with my legs and feet. She asked if I'd ever been in a marching band in high school. No, I hadn't. She explained that this is what people do when music comes on. It's called marking time, and everyone does it. Oh, I didn't know that.

One day, I brought along some music I'd been moving to at home to my ballet lesson. I told Karen that I wasn't sure what I was doing, and wanted to do it for her to see if she had an explanation. We turned the music on, and as I moved to it, Karen's smile got wider and wider. She clasped her hands at her chest and watched joyfully. When I finished, she exclaimed, "That's modern dance. You're doing interpretive dance."

"Well, good, because I decided this is what I want to do."

The first time I did interpretive dance in public was at a church service. Those attending expressed their appreciation and were complimentary. On the way home from the service, I was incredulous. I couldn't believe I'd done it. I recall exactly where I was on the freeway when I said out loud, "Who was that up there dancing?"

The voice inside my head replied immediately. "You were being danced."

My eyes welled up and tingles ran through my entire body. I had finally found my essence. At long last, I was being true to the color and texture of the thread I'd been given in the weaving of the tapestry of the universe. My consciousness expanded.

※ ※ ※

Selah:

stop and listen.

Study question: How has your consciousness changed regarding the intelligence of your heart, gut, and head at this midpoint of the book?

HEART RESPONSES	GUT RESPONSES	HEAD RESPONSES

8

The Circular Paradigm in Business

Holistic philosophy concepts featured: unity with self and others, intentionality, and the ways we're all teachers, students, and cocreators

The business world is slowly moving toward incorporating the circular paradigm. Terms such as *collaborative leadership, transparency, transformational leadership, servant leadership*, and *shared governance circles* are gaining prominence. Tom Rath's 2007 business-management best seller *StrengthsFinder* 2.0 emphasizes the power of developing and contributing our strengths instead of fixing our weaknesses. When we shift our focus accordingly, we provide the space and place for all employees to help transform themselves and the business. The traditional power gradient changes when we all recognize and begin acting on our potential to be empowered. Leadership transforms from *power over* to a more synergistic idea of *power sharing*, more in line with a servant leadership style. Earlier leadership styles were more invested in *power over*. We need to honor how far we've come. We need to honor all the work we've done to get here. Dismissing something as outdated or passé fails to acknowledge the necessary, and unavoidable, process that brought us to today.

How can the template be used in the business world? First, let's look at a huge corporation. It has multiple divisions, each of which may not even be aware of all the others. The template could be used to bring a sense of corporate wholeness to all involved. Seeing the big picture is essential to meeting the goals of the organization, and increases employees' sense of self-worth. It could look like figure 8.

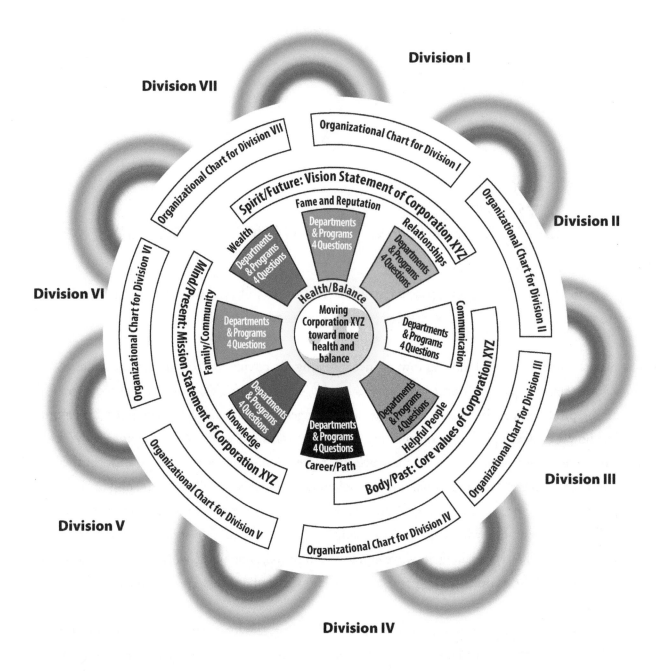

Division VII

Division I

Division II

Division VI

Division III

Division V

Division IV

Organizational Chart for Division VII

Organizational Chart for Division I

Organizational Chart for Division II

Organizational Chart for Division VI

Organizational Chart for Division III

Organizational Chart for Division V

Organizational Chart for Division IV

Spirit/Future: Vision Statement of Corporation XYZ

Mind/Present: Mission Statement of Corporation XYZ

Body/Past: Core values of Corporation XYZ

Fame and Reputation

Wealth

Relationships

Health/Balance

Family/Community

Communication

Moving Corporation XYZ toward more health and balance

Knowledge

Helpful People

Career/Path

Departments & Programs 4 Questions

Departments & Programs 4 Questions

Departments & Programs 4 Questions

Departments & Programs 4 Questions

Departments & Programs 4 Questions

Departments & Programs 4 Questions

Departments & Programs 4 Questions

Departments & Programs 4 Questions

Figure 8. Corporate mandala application.

Each division is named in the rainbow ring, and the corresponding organizational chart is shown in ring 2. The corporate values, mission, and vision are shown in ring 3. Ring 4 shows the departments and programs that speak to each life aspect, and could show the answers to four questions for each life aspect:

1. What is working?
2. What isn't working yet?
3. What goals do we have for developing departments or programs in this life aspect?
4. What are the priorities of these goals?

A digital version of this completed template for a corporation could be part of a website or on an information kiosk in the lobby, where those wanting information about the company could click on the areas they want to explore to access additional information.

Another business application could be to use the template to profile a potential customer or company prior to marketing to them. What are their seven sources or resources? What do you want to learn about those sources or resources? What are their values, mission, and vision statements? What departments and programs do they have for manifesting the life aspects?

Another business application for the template is as a tool for annual employee reviews. We talked above about focusing on strengths instead of weaknesses. People learn best when they are motivated from within. An annual appraisal, ideally, would be a learning opportunity for both the employee and the employer. Therefore, the employee could be asked to bring the following to the appraisal meeting:

Rainbow ring: List seven areas in which you excel.

Ring 2: List seven things you've improved on in the last year.

Ring 3: Describe three areas where you'd like to grow or learn more in the next year. (These may or may not be directly connected to body, mind, and spirit.)

Ring 4: Which life aspects of the company are you the best equipped to contribute toward, based on the information in the first three rings? Or, what suggestions do you have for the company in each life aspect? Is there something the company needs to develop?

I used a similar method for eight years with employees, and it never failed. They initiated the discussion of any performance problems or challenges. We then became intentional partners in how we viewed the desired goals; the process allowed us to become cocreators in a teaching and learning process.

Let's consider a clinical example that illustrates the concepts of unity with self and others; intentionality; and the ways we're all teachers, students, and cocreators. The personal life example follows the clinical example.

AN EYE FOR IMPROV

Fay, a physically fit ninety-year-old dementia client, never wanted to go out, but when she did, she really enjoyed it. It wasn't effective to invite her out or plan something with her because she'd just respond with "What for? No point in that." It was effective to help her with her coat, announce "Come on, we're going out," and start walking out the door with her. When she asked where we were going, it wasn't effective to tell her where. We'd just arrive at our planned destination, unsnap her seat belt, and help her out of the car while saying, "I need to see someone here," or something similar.

On one occasion, I'd made an ophthalmology appointment with Dr. Ray for her—with some trepidation, I might add. Fay was having recurrent eye infections and her nurse practitioner was uncomfortable with the apparent ineffectiveness of the meds and interventions being used. When I scheduled the appointment, I alerted the scheduler to the challenges of getting the client to their office.

When I picked up Fay, I asked the staff to call the doctor's office to let them know I was on my way, and if I didn't arrive, it was because I wasn't able to get her out of the car. Upon arrival in the parking ramp, Fay asked me where we were going. I told her I had a friend I wanted to see. She came right along. When we got to the office door, she read the name of Dr. Ray and thought it sounded familiar. I noted he was who I was there to see. She wondered why, and by then we were taking off our coats and checking in. The receptionist needed some forms filled out, so we sat down. I filled out the forms under Fay's persistent questioning of why we were there. I told her that since she has glaucoma, and my dad has glaucoma—and it runs in families—maybe my friend Dr. Ray would check both of us. This seemed to be an acceptable explanation. After I filled out the forms, I took them to the receptionist and quickly told her about my explanations to Fay. She nodded and said the word would be passed along to the doctor.

The wait was long and Fay almost lost her patience, deciding at one point we should go. I talked her out of it, and soon someone called my name. I stood up to go back to the exam room, and Fay came with me. I was told to sit in a specific chair, and Fay was told to sit in another. Soon Dr. Ray (whom I'd never met) entered the room, came over to me with a big grin, put out his hand, and said, "Ellen, so nice to see you again!" Then he greeted Fay, and we talked about her recognizing his name and that he likely saw her at his previous office, which was close to her former home. First, he "examined" my eyes and made a few comments. Then he checked Fay thoroughly. The whole visit went smoothly and he and his staff seemed to know just when to take charge or back off. Our shared good intentions forged a unity that allowed us to cocreate a successful therapeutic event for the reluctant Fay.

BODY AS TEACHER

Children do their best to make sense of things they don't quite understand. In the process, they can reach unintended conclusions and absorb mistaken beliefs. One conclusion I reached as a young child was that I shouldn't do anything my older brother Rod couldn't do. For example, since Rod couldn't dance, I shouldn't either. So I had to overcome two roadblocks to dancing. The first was the religious teaching that dance was a sin, but this second one was more personal. Rod is my oldest brother. In the 1940s and '50s, oldest brothers held a privileged place in families, and Rod was Number One in ours. I wasn't upset about that. In fact, in my child mind, I had to strategize ways to uphold that hierarchy because Rod was physically challenged. Perhaps that was the main source of my mistaken belief about dancing.

One night after I'd started dancing as an adult, a group came to a dance. They each wore a name tag featuring the name of their organization and an explanation: "We dance for those who can't." Tears streamed down my cheeks when I read this statement. This was a one-hundred-eighty-degree shift from my mistaken belief. I realized that, in part, I had unconsciously blamed not dancing on my oldest brother's physical condition. When we blame, we stagnate. We're stuck. I realized that I could free myself by erasing the blame tape and internalizing a new message: "I know something about being born into a family with a physically challenged child." That shift in perspective gave me permission to use that knowledge and experience instead of being shackled by it.

Shortly after my revelation that night, my dance teacher was teaching me a new step that involved turning one foot momentarily into a pigeon-toed position. My body wasn't cooperating, and I felt a profound sadness envelope me. What was going on? Then I understood. A person with clubfeet usually walks as if pigeon-toed. Rod had clubfeet. People sometimes made fun of him by mimicking his gait. My body didn't want to mock him as others did. This dancing revelation brought tears of compassion.

Tears cleanse. The chemical composition of tears changes based on the reason for the tears and what needs to be cleansed (Skorucak). Cleansing empties us so we can feel the heart fire within. As Irish poet and prominent twentieth-century literary figure William Butler Yeats said, "Education is not about filling a pail, but about lighting a fire" (Fox 1998, 1). The body is like a best friend. The more we listen to it, the more it tells and teaches us. We experience increased unity with self. This enables us to integrate more intentionality into our lives.

☀☀☀

Selah:

stop and listen.

YOUR RESPONSES AND NOTES

Study question: How comfortable are you letting your body be your teacher and cocreator?

HEART RESPONSES	GUT RESPONSES	HEAD RESPONSES

9

The Circular Paradigm in Life Events

Holistic philosophy concepts featured: verbal and nonverbal communication, transpersonal connections (connecting with another at a deeper level than the typical biological and ego states), and transcendental connections (going beyond the transpersonal to include the supernatural, mystical, or metaphysical)

In this chapter, we'll explore some life events in which the circular paradigm can be applied. The entire life continuum from birth to death is included, so there is something for everyone. You may want to use a copy of the worksheet provided at the end of the book for life events that you want to explore.

REUNIONS AND DEATHS

At a family reunion some years ago, we participated in a group activity in which we all talked about one of our ancestors and what memories we had of her. It was both enjoyable and informative—and incited gales of laughter alongside deep, meaningful appreciation. We could see that some of us were apples that hadn't fallen far from her tree. She taught some of us lessons that were different from those she taught others. It helped us all appreciate our individuality and our own unique relationship with this ancestor.

Some time later, I was talking with a friend who'd recently experienced a death in the family. There was the upcoming family gathering to be planned and experienced. After the conversation, I thought about my friend's grief and recalled the family reunion exercise—and inevitably contemplated how it connected to the circular template that was emerging in my thinking. Then I saw a connection, how the circular paradigm might be used in more informal and verbal ways. Often during times of funeral planning, families meet with clergy or speakers to discuss the eulogy. The circular template could provide a guide for that planning. Families also simply find comfort in gathering over a meal or sitting around a fire to share memories of the deceased. In either case, the rings of the template could facilitate the discussion. I'm not proposing a rigid adherence to the template at these times—but I am suggesting that it could provide a little structure at an emotional period. In those moments, these template questions may offer some helpful direction and focus:

1. What were the resources or sources of energy for the deceased? What energized him or her?

2. What did you learn from the deceased? What was he or she good at teaching and how did he or she teach? Were these teachings related to what energized him or her?

3. Describe the body, mind, and spirit of the deceased. It may be revealing how different the perceptions and experiences are among those gathered.

4. What were the values of the deceased in each of the life aspects?

Remember that in these circumstances, these gathered memories and anecdotes need to be seen as just information, not proof of who is right or wrong.

I learned from a successfully married couple that differences in perceptions and experiences are opportunities for increasing healthy intimacy. He told his interpretation of an event and she said she didn't experience it that way. He responded with, "Really? Tell me how you experienced it so I can get to know you better."

Discussion of the information garnered in the four rings above can reveal just how different the perceptions are among those gathered. Information about the deceased, the self, and others present could result. All this information could provide fodder for valuable family insights that could lead to experiencing an increased sense of family, rootedness, and belonging. A sense of the unique contributions of each family member may be enhanced and honored. More information on family values may be discovered.

In his book *Ethical Wills: Putting Your Values on Paper*, Dr. Barry K. Baines asserts that this kind of exploration of values is akin to an ethical will, a way to bequeath values rather than valuables. If the deceased has not written an ethical will prior to his or her passing, a family's exploration of the values they saw in the relative can become the ethical will. An articulation of those values can provide a nice insert in the program for the funeral, or a handout at the wake. It also establishes a sense of honored connection with the family member who has passed.

CHILDREN AND PARENTING

While visiting with the young vice president of a family business about how the circular template might be useful for his company, I was facing a blank wall in his new office. I suggested it would be a great place for his finished company template. We laughed about the implication that his walls needed anything other than pictures of his beautiful family, which graced the other walls.

I smiled when I recalled that on the drive home. Then suddenly I envisioned the company template application surrounded by separate templates for each of his children. The template of a child could be a growing depiction that unfolds as the child grows. Or a template could describe a specific year or period in a child's life, and be labeled as such.

Rainbow ring: What are the resources or sources that energize the child? What is he or she drawn to explore the most? A toy, a game, a hobby, a concept, a pet, a place, etc.?

Ring 2: What did the child seem to learn from each of the listed sources? Did he or she attempt to teach a sibling or peer something from that source of energy? If so, what?

Ring 3: Describe the body, mind, and spirit of the child.

Ring 4: What seems most important to the child in each of the life aspects?

Center: As a variation for this application, the center might be used for a photo of the child.

Having a child's developmental history diagrammed in this way could be meaningful and enlightening.

I imagine it would help the child make a grounded exploration of him- or herself at any age or stage of development. Perhaps it brings the baby book of yore into the current century. Maybe the process of creating periodical circular templates would also help expand the child's concept of the self beyond a hierarchical viewpoint early enough in life to make the nonhierarchical more ingrained. As Jung describes, the mandala serves to reunify the self. (*Webster's*, 870). It could be said that it embraces the essence of the person.

I believe this could also bring about a more healthy intimacy in family relationships. I was in a class in the early 1980s in which the teacher claimed that 95 percent of Americans were afraid of healthy intimacy. Then she proceeded in her lecture. I put up my hand to stop her. I said I could accept that I was probably one of the 95 percent—but, I wanted to know, just exactly how would she define what I'm supposedly afraid of? She proceeded to compare healthy intimacy to the base camp of a mountain climb. Each day, family members go out and climb their own mountains. They come back to base camp at night and ask each other about the day's climb. At no time, however, does one try and climb the mountain of the other person. You support them in climbing their own mountains. This builds self-confidence in children. It also teaches healthy boundaries and self-responsibility.

It's possible for us each to "climb our own mountain" but remain part of a tight-knit team if the energy sources; consequent learnings; uniquenesses of body, mind, and spirit; and values in all life aspects of each person are recognized and honored. To be successful, though, the circular self-enhancing energy that comes from interdependence, mutuality, and synergy must be part of the equation. In the traditional hierarchical paradigm, conformity is mandatory, while individuality is a threat. The challenge is to move to community without conformity.

RELATIONSHIPS AND MARRIAGES

The same questions apply to adult relationships, but the adult relationship can take it all one step further. Individual application of the mandala template to oneself is the first step. The next step is to apply it to your partner to see how well you know him or her, and vice versa. This practice may be useful in premarital counseling and marriage renewal, using questions such as:

Rainbow ring: What are my resources or sources of energy? What gives me energy, feeds my soul, pushes my blade of grass up through the concrete of life?

Ring 2: What have I learned from these sources? What do I teach from these sources?

Ring 3: How do I describe my body, mind, and spirit as of today?

Ring 4: What do I value in each life aspect? What is working and what isn't working yet in each life aspect? Where do I want to go in each area?

When you complete the process for yourself, do the same thing for your partner. Then do the same for your relationship, as though the relationship is a third person in your partnership. Partners could do the relationship application separately and then share, or the partners could do the relationship application together.

Rainbow ring: What are the resources or sources of energy that feed our partnership? What inspires our togetherness?

Ring 2: What have we learned from these resources or sources?

Ring 3: How do we describe the body, mind, and spirit of our relationship? You may consider seeing the body as the past, the mind as the present, and the spirit as the future of the relationship.

Ring 4: What are the values we share in each life aspect? You could also determine the joys, goals, concerns, and thoughts you both have in common in these life aspects.

The following clinical example includes the concepts of verbal and nonverbal communication. The personal, everyday-life example demonstrates connecting at transpersonal and transcendental levels. Often these experiences of nonverbal communication as well as transpersonal and transcendental connections seem mystical and mysterious. If we're open to the mystical and mysterious—if we don't always need provable answers to everything—these experiences can fill us with awe and wonder. Then instead of doubting, we can be inspired.

PHANTOM PEACE

"Can you help my client die peacefully?" my colleague Carol asked from the other end of the phone line. Carol explained that her client was actively dying in hospice and was thrashing and moaning no matter what was done for her. She thought maybe I could try the new approach I was studying, called Healing Touch. I was certainly willing to attempt to improve the dying woman's experience. This was in the mid-1990s, before such alternative therapies were as accepted or as well known as they are now, twenty years later.

I went to visit Mary in the hospice facility without delay. Carol had arranged for my arrival. As the hospice nurse talked with me outside Mary's door, I learned that Mary was a retired teacher. I was surprised to also learn that Mary was in protective precautions, meaning a mask and gloves were advised for the nurse's protection. If this was going to work, the last thing Mary would feel and see, if she perchance opened her eyes, would be a gloved touch and a masked face. I immediately ruled out that possibility and imagined an invisible protective energetic shield around me instead. I entered Mary's room and, indeed, she was moaning and thrashing with discomfort, and her mental state was what I would call semicomatose. I prepared myself for the work by energizing my hands. Since one basic principle of using this technique is that energy follows intent, I set the intention for comfort and a peaceful passing.

I went to her left side and began a technique that involved touching her in long, calming, light strokes down her limbs and trunk. My intention was to brush off any old anxieties and pressures that may be causing the discomfort. After several strokes, her moans began to soften. After work on the left side was complete, her thrashing had calmed considerably. I went to her right side. I started with the arm, down the trunk, and then got to the leg.

A second surprise awaited me. I wasn't told that she'd had a leg amputation just above her right knee. I was starting my first stroke down that leg and suddenly the leg was not there. My mind flashed quickly to knowledge, followed by an intuition. Amputees often report what's called phantom pain, where they feel pain in the missing part of the limb. Therefore, I continued on down the leg as though it was

76

still there. Her moan changed significantly. It was almost as though it became a purr of relief. If a moan could transform to a thank-you, this would have been it. As I continued working on the phantom leg, she became calm and her purrs were softer and softer. No more moans. I then went to the top of her head and began to spread each energy center down her body, which is a technique used to help with transitions. I then returned to her left side and very, very, lightly began the stroking technique again. Her breaths came more slowly. I was barely brushing her upper limb, with the intention of moving the energy up into the heavens, when she took three very deep long breaths and stopped breathing. I backed away so she could leave her body without interference.

Soon I turned on her call light and the hospice nurse came in. She looked at Mary and then at me. I smiled softly and nodded. She listened to Mary's heart, nodded, quietly expressed appreciation, and left the room.

I did my typical closure, spiritually blessing the person onward in their journey, and left the room. The hospice administrator was awaiting me in the hallway. He looked at me and said he understood Mary had left in a most beautiful manner. I asked him what that was. He said, "She was getting a massage." I nodded and smiled. I knew she had gotten an energy massage, and that her heart was now at peace, reunited with her phantom leg. My job in those moments was to understand her needs from nonverbal signals she gave. And she communicated, quite clearly, without the benefit of words.

SAYING GOOD-BYE

In June 2007, it was apparent that Dad would soon be leaving us. He had lived in the world of Alzheimer's for ten years. It was a long, slow, and sometimes painful good-bye. I have always seen the dying journey to be an opportunity to midwife someone into the next life—an apt metaphor since it was a nine-month process. During this June visit to Mom and Dad in Indiana, I suggested to Mom that we write an ethical will for Dad. Doctor and author Barry K. Baines suggests that when a person has not and is no longer capable of writing their own ethical will, the family write it for him or her. Mom and I worked on some ideas, and I brought them home with me to Minneapolis and typed them into an ethical will. I went to my paper supply above my head in my den closet, and my hand went right to one slot. I pulled the paper out and looked at the design, shrugged my shoulders, and said, "Okay, whatever." I printed up enough copies to hand out at the wake, put them in a file folder, and added it to my "emergency trip to Indiana" bag.

In November 2007, during one of my weekly calls to Mom, she said she knew Dad was really gone then. I asked her how she knew. She said, "Well, he has always puckered when I kiss him. He doesn't pucker anymore." We grieved together. After ending the call, I sat with this information, and then nodded decisively.

As his health-care power of attorney, I'd always wondered how I would know when to implement Dad's advance directive to stop further use of antibiotics. I called his doctor in Indiana. I reviewed the conversation with Mom. I told the doctor of my conclusion. She agreed wholeheartedly. No more antibiotics. Then I called my two brothers and Dad's two younger sisters. All were in agreement. I called Mom back to tell her of the consensus, and she completely agreed.

Nine months after typing up the ethical will, on March 12, 2008, one of Dad's nurses called me. He had two infections going on, maybe three, and the doctor wasn't ordering antibiotics. Did I want to intervene? I told her about our decision, and referred her to the advance directives in Dad's chart. We called in hospice. Dad passed peacefully and comfortably on March 15, with Mom at his side singing, "Let Me Call You Sweetheart."

When I heard the news, I went to my emergency-trip bag and made sure everything was ready to go. I pulled out the file with the ethical will and looked at it. My body broke out in tingles all over. Nine months previously, I had printed Dad's ethical will on paper celebrating St. Patrick's Day, March 17. The paper had shamrocks and an Irish prayer printed around the border: "May the road rise to meet you. May the wind be always at your back. May the sun shine warm upon your face. And may rains fall soft upon your fields. And until we meet again, May God keep you in the hallow of his hand."

※※※

Selah:

stop and listen.

Study question: When you have experiences of awe, mystery, and wonder, can you identify when to hold them silently in your heart, and when you're ready to share them?

HEART RESPONSES	GUT RESPONSES	HEAD RESPONSES

10

The Circular Paradigm in Health Care

Holistic philosophy concepts featured: empirical, innate, intuitive, and reflective knowledge

One of the first things we do in health care when someone comes to us is assess their health status. I prefer to think of this as accessing the client. This idea echoes the nursing theory of modeling and role-modeling's suggestion that we seek to understand the client's model of their own world (Erickson, Tomlin, and Swain, 97). When you access a person, you walk a mile in their shoes, so to speak. That's why presence, connecting or joining, using the felt sense, relationship-as-intervention, and listening from the heart (i.e., with body intelligence) are essential tools. I don't know how a health-care provider can access a client without these tools.

If the circular template isn't a practical tool for this, it offers a definite conceptual benefit. Instead of perceiving of the client in a linear fashion, superior or inferior, we can more easily embrace their essence and thus their model of their world. There are several ways to apply the template. The first option uses empirical knowledge and incorporates intuitive, innate, body intelligence/felt sense, and reflective knowledge.

Rainbow ring: Divide the body up into seven systems (empirical knowledge).

1. Gastrointestinal
2. Respiratory/circulatory
3. Nervous
4. Musculoskeletal
5. Genitourinary
6. Endocrine/immune
7. Ear, eye, nose, throat

Ring 2: Assessment and diagnostic information for each system (what you learned about the client). The space under the rainbows could be used to include the intuitive, innate, body intelligence/felt sense, and reflective knowledge. (These truly can be pots of gold, as we will soon see in an example.)

Ring 3: Plan of care for body, mind (includes emotions), and spirit.

Ring 4: The goals for, or how the plan manifests in, each life aspect.

The second application option would be based more in the social services approach.

Rainbow ring: The client's resources or sources, such as people, organizations, interests, etc.

Ring 2: What each resource or source provides and the contact information for each. Again, use the space under the rainbows to include the intuitive, innate, body intelligence/felt sense, and reflective knowledge. (These pots of gold can save lives physically, as well as relationally.)

Ring 3: Social service plan of care for the body, mind (includes emotions), and spirit.

Ring 4: The goals for, or how the plan manifests in, each life aspect.

Historically, our downfall has been to use only the empirical and linear knowledge we gain in such information gathering, whether initially in the assessment or in the ongoing care of the client. Equally important are the intuitive, innate, body intelligence/felt sense, and reflective sources from within the client *and* the health-care practitioner. The following clinical illustration shows how important this can be.

JUST THE FACTS, MA'AM

It all started in my first year of practice in 1969. I worked the three-to-eleven shift on a unit with three hallways. It was a small hospital in a town of about twenty-five thousand, and progressive for the time. One of the three hallways was for minimal-care patients. These were people coming in for minor surgeries or testing procedures requiring preps that are now done at home.

One of my patients on the minimal-care wing had been through two surgeries that day: a dilation and curettage (D&C) and a hemorrhoidectomy. Several hours into the shift, although her vital signs remained normal and her pad was dry, I felt something wasn't quite right. I called her physician and told him about the normal data and my (felt) sense of something being off. He chose to rely on the data. I called him two more times during the shift with the same concerns. The data remained fine, but my unease increased with each passing hour. I informed the oncoming nurse and went home at the end of my shift.

When I returned to work the next day, the patient wasn't there. I immediately asked about her. She'd been taken back to surgery during the night and was transferred to the surgical unit afterward. No sooner did I learn this than her physician came onto the unit looking for me. "Miss Hernley," he said, "from now on, I'll listen to you the first time you call." It turned out the patient had a large hematoma in the rectal area that was blocking off the proximal end of the cervix, not allowing a uterine hemorrhage to drain. Plus, the rectal hematoma was pressing on her vagus nerve, which explained why there were no vital sign changes indicating shock.

Modern medicine—and more broadly, modern society—have relied on the facts and metrics, head intelligence, allowing them to trump body intelligence/felt sense, intuition, as well as innate and reflective intelligence. There are consequences that can be life threatening as well as relationship threatening.

How might an integration of scientific (empirical and linear) and nonscientific (intuitive, innate, and reflective) knowledge look in an everyday life situation? Notice the knowledge collaboration that took place in this example.

IT'S THE KELP

My friend Sally had recently returned from a sea-kayaking trip. We were walking around the lake and she was telling me about her trip. I knew nothing about this type of adventure, and I was eager to hear about it.

She'd been using many alternative treatment approaches to a skin condition on her hands and arms, sometimes clearing it and then having it recur. We had puzzled over it together for weeks prior to her trip.

She talked about the various adventures of the trip. Then she said that part of the way through the trip, she noticed her skin condition had cleared up. Suddenly I heard myself say, "Sally, it's the kelp." She turned to me and said, "Oh, so then you do know about sea kayaking." I told her I didn't know where those words came from, and no, I didn't know anything about sea kayaking. She explained that when sea kayakers need a rest, they find a bed of kelp and grab onto a strand with an outstretched hand. Since it's rooted in the ocean floor, you're anchored and can rest from paddling without worrying about drifting with the current. Although the kelp is firm, she told me, it's also slippery.

Upon hearing this, I concluded that kelp slipperiness would likely mean it was mucilaginous (producing mucilage, a gelatinous substance created by some plants) and could therefore be soothing to the skin. This, combined with Sally's other treatments and the sunshine and saltwater, could have made a difference. Florence Nightingale promoted many remedies such as sunshine, fresh air, and the provisions of nature.

❀❀❀

Selah:

stop and listen.

Study question: How do all forms of knowledge (empirical, innate, intuitive, and reflective) connect to the famous *Star Wars* quote, "May the Force be with you"?

HEART RESPONSES	GUT RESPONSES	HEAD RESPONSES

11

The Circular Paradigm in Addiction Treatment

Holistic philosophy concepts featured: observation, pattern manifestation, self-knowledge, and walk the talk

Addiction has a direct link to the hierarchy. Renowned addiction specialist and author Anne Wilson Schaef speaks saliently to this link in two of her books, *When Society Becomes an Addict* (1987, 94–5) and *The Addictive Organization* (1988, 3). According to Schaef, "The Addictive System is based upon the illusion of control, the illusion of perfectionism, thinking processes that twist reality into left-brain constructs, dishonesty, and denial." (1987, 94). These can all be characteristics of the hierarchical approach.

Table 1 in Chapter 2 organizes and reviews the paradigm characteristics of the current linear paradigm alongside the characteristics of the emerging circular paradigm. That table lists over- and under-responsible behaviors and attitudes as part of the linear paradigm's modus operandi. An exess of these behaviors and attitudes are commonly found in addictive family systems, which is understandable since over-responsible people fit hand-in-glove with under-responsible people. Both have unhealthy needs the other can fill and neither is healthily self-responsible. The dynamic often follows the same pattern: the addict is under-responsible and the enabler is over-responsible. Neither have clear boundaries for themselves or the other and they share confusion about where one person ends and the other begins. Boundary invasions can occur physically, mentally, emotionally, and spiritually. This form of relating often carries from one generation to the next, until consciousness rises and someone risks breaking the pattern.

Table 2 can help you understand the holistic concepts featured in this chapter. It gives you a chance to observe patterns in yourself, gain self-knowledge, and walk the talk of self-responsibility. You may recognize yourself in one column in one row, and another column in the next row. As humans, we aren't necessarily consistent.

Table 2. Responsibility—Where Are You?

UNDER-RESPONSIBLE (often unconscious, victim, invaded)	SELF-RESPONSIBLE (more conscious and respectful)	OVER-RESPONSIBLE (unconscious, invasive, controlling)
1. I am lovable only if you approve of me.	1. I love myself; therefore I can truly love others.	1. You are a reflection of me. You are lovable only if I approve of you.
2. I depend on you to make me whole. I admit to my weaknesses, but not my strengths.	2. I admit to both my strengths and challenges. It's OK for me to be human.	2. I must shape you up in order for me to be all right. I focus on your weaknesses.
3. You are always right; I rarely am right. I concentrate on your strengths.	3. I can see both strengths and challenges in other people. It's OK for you to be human.	3. I cannot admit the weaknesses in myself; therefore I must always look strong.
4. Things are really hopeless. No one can help me.	4. I can ask others for help.	4. I need to be perfect; therefore I must turn away support and assistance when I need it.
5. I am helpless; therefore you must take care of me. You take consequences for me.	5. I am responsible for my own actions, and can accept my consequences.	5. I am responsible for your actions. I take consequences that belong to you.
6. I can't be different. I must please, be approved of.	6. I can be different and allow others to be different from me.	6. If you are different than I want you to be, I will blame, accuse, reject, etc. you.
7. I am afraid to talk to you because you are always right. Whatever I say will be wrong.	7. I can be honest about my feelings and who I am. I allow you to do the same.	7. Since I must be strong, I cannot share my real feelings.
8. I must always do what people ask of me. I cannot say "no."	8. I can trust myself, my expressions, my abilities, and my decisions.	8. You do not do things my way (the right way) so I must do them for you.
9. It is not safe to be clear, so I must manipulate to get what I want.	9. I know when I can trust other people.	9. I can't trust others to be clear, so problems are all their fault.
10. I will surely fail; therefore I can't take risks, so why try?	10. I can take risks.	10. I can't let you take risks.
11. My needs will never be met because they are not important. I am sub-human, inferior.	11. My needs are important–they are a part of me.	11. I do not have personal needs. I am superhuman, superior.

I organized this information after studying many sources and attending multiple meetings and classes in the 1980s when the buzzword was *codependency*. Codependents enable an addictive lifestyle and family system. Under-responsible behavior is often unconscious, and the under-responsible person feels invaded and victimized—the classic expressions of *dependence*, which is one of the three key aspects of the linear paradigm's emphasis (along with *independence and money*.) Over-responsible behavior is also often unconscious, and the over-responsible person can be experienced as invasive and controlling, which can be interpreted as unhealthy independence. These approaches are typical of and enhanced by the hierarchical paradigm. Self-responsible behavior is more conscious and respectful, emphasizing interdependence, mutuality, and synergy. Self-responsibility requires a true clarity of the self, a strong sense of self-ownership, which occurs as a result of healthy independence. According to Stephen Covey, only then is the interdependence of the emerging paradigm possible (2004, 186).

Some experts define addiction as an internal response to external forces—meaning addicts seek comfort from any number of sources outside the self. Addiction language refers to this as external referencing. Focus on these outside sources numbs the pain and feelings of the past and/or the present life. These outside sources can be substances or behaviors—which include, but are not limited to, chemicals such as alcohol, nicotine, and caffeine; drugs; workaholism; gambling; food; sex; clothing; shopping; video games; computers and technology toys; a relationship or person; money; religion; power; exercise; etc.

The crux of the problem lies in an *unbalanced* lifestyle and the outside source becoming the person's source of comfort, or Higher Power. The life of the addict is consumed by the outside source. An inordinate amount of time and money goes into focusing on this source, until other aspects of life cease to be tended to, or sometimes seemingly cease to exist or matter. The result is an unhealthy body, a mind in denial of reality, emotions that are numb and repressed or suppressed, and a spirit that is dying. When emotions are numbed, one needs extremes to be able to feel. Violence, dominance, control, and power are hierarchical extremes that are destructive to the self, others, organizations, and society.

Visual representations can be helpful in understanding how all this cycles into self-destruction. Keep in mind that cycles are circles, and circles have a self-perpetuating energy. This is why addicts cycle down deeper and deeper into destruction. Then the circle's energy is locked in like a tornado or cyclone, both of which result in destruction. This next visual, figure 9, is called the substance abuse cycle.

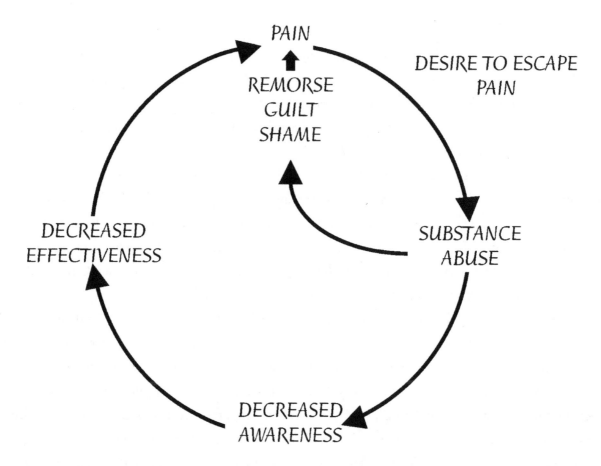

Figure 9. Substance abuse cycle.

I'll review this cycle while simultaneously repeating some of the above information in different words, since this is a soft science and sometimes different words are needed for comprehension. See if this helps.

A progression to desperation develops when we get out of balance and depend too much on any one substance, behavior, or person. Starting with the outer cycle, this dependency can develop because, consciously or unconsciously, we want to escape pain (physical, mental, emotional, spiritual, or relationship pain). So we look for a high, or a comfort source, in something outside ourselves. When we focus on externals, we're less aware of our own pain. However, when we're less aware, we're also less effective, and know that, at some level. This causes even more pain. In the meantime, on the inside, every time the substance is abused, feelings of shame, guilt, and remorse crop up. This also causes even more pain. In other words, every time pain or feelings are not dealt with in a healthy way, our pain is compounded.

How does this look when the dependency is on another person? This can include a concept called "guru-itis." Again, there is the hand-in-glove fit. One person is compelled to be a guru, an authority over others, while their followers need a guru, an external authority on whom they want to depend and cling. Those needing a guru are often projecting onto the guru positive characteristics they cannot yet own in themselves. This next visual, figure 10, illustrates dependency on another person, the personal abuse cycle.

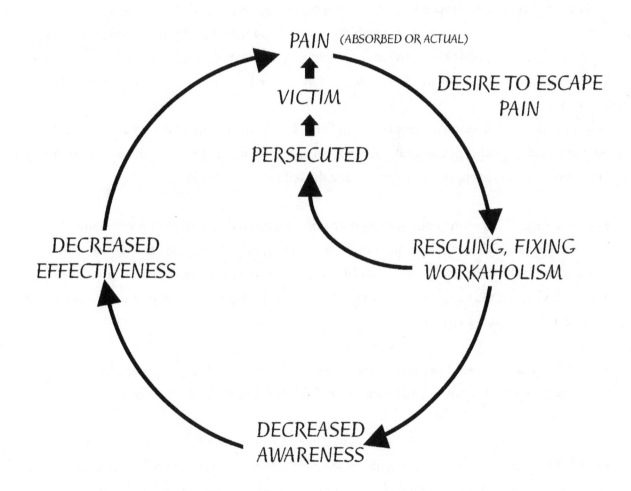

Figure 10. Personal abuse cycle.

Figure 10 illustrates a desire to escape pain, one's own pain, or someone else's pain that is absorbed. Those individuals caught in a cycle of "fixing" others can easily fall into a kind of rescue workaholism that circles around and around. When they're focused intently on others, their own awareness of pain, actual or absorbed, lessens. Less awareness begets less effectiveness, and knowing this at some level, causes even more pain. Simultaneously, on the inside, when one becomes a workaholic at fixing and rescuing someone else, and it doesn't work, one starts to feel persecuted and victimized for all that isn't appreciated. Every time pain or feelings are not dealt with in a healthy way, the pain is compounded, leading to a downward cycle into destruction. There is a frantic feeling, and this leads to an underlying "binge mentality" in an unconscious attempt to numb the pain. The binge mentality is applied to most aspects of the person's life; eating, drinking, driving fast, exercising, over-scheduling, workaholism, hunger for power, etc. Some of these potentially problematic behaviors are not only socially sanctioned and encouraged, but even required.

How does the holistic mandala template fit in here? The template could be used as an individual "know thyself and thy dependency" tool. Observation and pattern manifestation are helpful in this process. The person begins to engage in looking inside the self instead of externally.

Rainbow ring: What sources or resources both encourage and discourage substance abuse for the particular individual? That question is the first step in looking inside for answers, understanding, and self-knowledge; what has brought shame and denial in the past can now be redefined. Owning the truth can now be visualized as a pot of gold at the end of the rainbow. Remember the power of visuals.

Ring 2: What was learned from each of these sources, about the self, about dependency, about the source? What can be taught and how? (This is where walking the talk comes into play.)

Ring 3: Here the person has an opportunity to describe how the dependency has affected their body, mind, and spirit, and/or what resources their body, mind, and spirit contribute to their recovery.

Ring 4: Dependency has affected all aspects of life. Here the person gets to clearly state how each life aspect has been affected, and what kind of self-care is needed to heal. There is a sense of relief that eases the need to deny through binge-mentality behaviors.

Reunification of the self occurs when the denial is exposed, faced, owned, and acknowledged to the self and others. Integration of the self occurs when the person grasps the Higher Power within, at their very center, and relies on that instead of the substance. Then there is growth toward a healthier balance represented by the yin and yang symbol in the center. Self-care is crucial in bringing this about.

Mandalas allow energy to flow from inside to outside and from outside to inside and throughout the entire visual. Nothing is locked in. The self-sustaining energy of the circle becomes constructive when there is reunification with the self and integration of the self. Then the person can begin to walk the talk by putting into practice what they speak, by making words and actions congruent. The old saw that actions speak louder than words is eternal: walking the path gets you farther than just talking about the path.

The mandala template also could be used as a course syllabus about addictions for those in an educational program to become chemical dependency counselors. As a digital interactive model, it could have the course content for courses on addiction.

The next story relates a clinical experience that incorporates this chapter's holistic concepts of observation, pattern manifestation, self-knowledge, and walking the talk. It's followed by a personal anecdote that incorporates these holistic concepts.

YOU CAN'T HELP ME!

I was in orientation for a new nursing job. I had wanted to work on a unit for eating disorders at a local hospital. I'd finished my first three days when the nurses went on strike. At the end of the strike, the only openings left were on the sexual addiction unit. That orientation was extensive, since this was a relatively new specialty in mental health at that time. The orientation included nurses, physicians, psychologists, and social workers. We had to take all the diagnostic tests given to those admitted to the unit. We had to discover where we were on the continuum of addict to coaddict. Self-knowledge was a requirement of the job. We were to observe ourselves, look for pattern manifestation, and be able to walk the talk to model for our patients. Discussing our test results in small groups of orientees was part of the process. We were to understand what our clients would experience at a very deep level. We couldn't help people come out of denial if we were in denial ourselves.

Many of the clients on the unit were there for being perpetrators. Most had been abused as children, and they came from all professions and walks of life. Twelve-step group participation was part of the recovery process for all of our patients, and transparency and mutuality has been a practice in twelve-step programs for decades. The unit's team needed to understand the process fully, and our orientation was filled with exercises to help us do just that.

The most memorable part of the orientation was from a panel discussion. The panel consisted of those who had been through the treatment program and were now home, functioning in society. Their main point: "If you have not done your work on this issue, you can't help me or anyone on the unit!" They had observed themselves for patterns and gained self-knowledge and were now walking the talk.

This aligned exactly with how I practiced. I tried to keep one foot in the client's world and one in my world. I tried to keep my left brain in my scientific knowledge world and my right brain and heart in the client's world. This is what the panel said had to happen in order for us to help them. Perfect fit!

WHAT DO YOU WANT TO BE WHEN YOU GROW UP?

When I was asked this question as a child, I could only imagine that I wanted to do something that required lots of physical discipline, but I didn't want to be a gym teacher. I wouldn't dare consciously think of the word *dance*. Dancing was a sin, after all, because it led to sex. By age fifty-two, when I finally started dancing, I was well aware that if sex is on someone's mind, then just about anything can lead to sex, but that wouldn't have occurred to me as a child. In my college years, I was very interested in psychology, but the conservative fundamentalist religion of my parents taught me that psychology was the work of the devil. Yet here I am, years later, writing a book that converses with lots of notions central to the field of psychology.

In retrospect, had my upbringing been different, I concluded I would likely have been a dance therapist. I've felt wistful about that at times, wondering what that would have felt like. Then I was given the gift of finding out.

I was doing a dance program for a church-connected assisted living facility in another state. I was dancing songs familiar to the persons present, and relating the songs to the seasons of their lives. For example, "This Little Light of Mine" depicts the light that the birth of an infant brings to a family, as well as the energy of a child discovering life. When we marry and move into our own homes, "Bless This House" memorializes that life event. "Sunrise, Sunset" takes us through the span of life, and "On Eagle's Wings" lifts us in our transition to the next life. During this particular program, about half the people were tearful. One resident came up afterward and said it was a four-Kleenex program. After everyone had left, I turned to the chaplain and resident coordinator and social worker, and saw their tears. "You two, too?" I exclaimed. They explained to me that they knew these people so well. They had worked with them daily for years. The woman who'd said it was a four-Kleenex program was one they had been trying to get to express a feeling, any feeling, for two years. In their eyes, this was a miracle for her.

It was a miracle for me as well. I felt a fulfillment I never expected to experience. This was one of the final healings in my recovery from food addiction. In the three-day orientation on the eating disorders unit, I learned through observation, identifying pattern manifestation, and applying personal knowledge, that I was a food addict. I had used food as a substance for years, repressing the pain of not being able to pursue dance or psychology.

❦ ❦ ❦

Selah:

stop and listen.

Study question: What pattern manifestations do you now observe in yourself? What consequences do you see from them?

HEART RESPONSES	GUT RESPONSES	HEAD RESPONSES

12

Merging the Two Paradigms

Holistic philosophy concepts featured: integrative practices and health as an expression of life process

Now we get to the heart of this work. The heart is where circulation is managed in the human body. Circulation is circular, and includes movement and flow, repair and growth. Heart energy is the circular energy of life. Yet it cannot act alone. It must interact with many other body parts, including linear ones, to perform its vital function. When all our parts work together, they create an effect that is greater than the sum of these parts. When each part contributes its best, the creative effort produces a synergistic result none could achieve on its own or even by simple addition.

We've already unconsciously merged the linear and circular in several ways. In table 1 in Chapter 2, look at the third line listing focus/brain/energy. The energy of the linear is electrical. The energy of the circular is magnetic. We already have electromagnetic energy. We unconsciously began the merger long ago when we came up with electromagnetic energy. How can we consciously merge the two paradigms? Respectfully.

First, the linear needs to be strengthened in a healthy manner. Think about electricity or rivers and how they need to have transformers or tributaries boost their power as they travel. Think about the Interstate 35W bridge across the Mississippi River in Minneapolis. It was a linear structure with gusset plates that rusted and led to its collapse. Now think about the bridges that last centuries. They are stone-arch bridges that resemble figure 11.

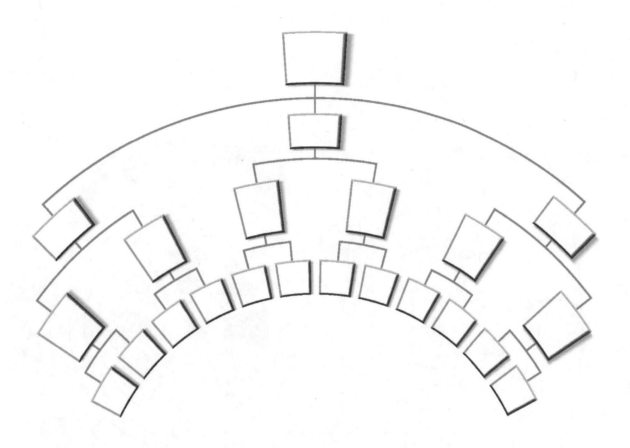

Figure 11. A healthier linear template.

The slight curvature lends the bridge strength and staying power because there is more flexibility in distribution of weight. In the traditional linear model, strength is constantly tested by rigidity needs. Strength needs are also impacted by variances in weight load. The flexibility in the curved model allows for the slight shifts that have to happen in weathering the literal and figurative storms that come along. Thus, the stone-arch bridge model is stronger in a healthier way.

At this point, aided by creativity, we are ready to merge the two paradigms in a healthier manner, and again we find we have already done this unconsciously. Figure 12 has the appearance of a satellite and leads us to embrace the future.

Figure 12. Merging two paradigms, step one.

The mandala is the sending and receiving dish of the satellite. There is figurative significance in sending and receiving the characteristics of the circular. The stone-arch bridge provides the energy panels. Satellites have a few jets at the rear that keep them on course, making small directional corrections when needed. Stephen Covey notes that the job of leadership is to be sure the ladder everyone is climbing leans against the correct wall, or the jungle everyone is chopping through is the right jungle (2004, 101). Much like a satellite's course-correcting engines, leaders then become the power *behind*, not power *over*. The leader provides direction for the creative force of synergy, which combines the best self-responsible contributions all can muster.

Power changes like this don't occur overnight. Remember there is a long history of suppression by the hierarchical "power over" modus operandi. Pendulums don't swing to center immediately. It takes them awhile to get there. It will be important to have compassion and give the circular paradigm some time to heal from all that suppression, and the linear paradigm time to get adjusted to and feel appreciation for its healthier self. Healing is a sacred process, and when deep healing genuinely occurs, it always includes compassion. Perhaps we could use an interim visual where this healing could occur. Figure 13 is offered as a possible healing visual.

Figure 13. Merging two paradigms, step two.

Here the stone-arch bridge has become a container. A container with no contents is empty. Contents with no container float away and disappear. Together in this fashion, the Holy Grail is visible. The sacredness of the union is available. There needs to be gratitude for the other as each paradigm does its healing work.

At some point, there is a readiness for the final phase where we come back to the beginning from which all originally sprang forth. We, as imperfect human beings, intermittently experience the pendulum at center. We do the best we can to recognize the sacred union in each of us and between us. In this sacred garden, we blossom and grow. Figure 14 depicts this original and final phase.

Figure 14. Nature's merger, step three.

Figure 14 is nature's paradigm. The female symbol and the male symbol on the left are used by the medical professions as shorthand for the female (top) and male (bottom). We all have feminine and masculine energy in us, regardless of gender, and balance is improved when we recognize this. Look what happens when the masculine and feminine energies integrate—we're capable of growing flowers full of awe, mystery, and wonder. That's when we'll know the energizing potential, the *miracles*, of synergy. Perhaps our vision for the future could be that we tend our shared garden and work to flower together in ways that express the process of health in the most holistic sense.

A Guinean proverb reminds us, "Judge each day, not by the harvest, but by the seeds you plant" (Miller). What "flower" seeds are you planting? How does your garden grow?

The following clinical example shows a variety of ways the merger of the two paradigms occurs when Western medicine and alternative practices are combined and health is expressed as a life process, not a product. A process is ongoing, and to be healthy we must flow with that ongoing process instead of expecting products in the form of quick fixes. The personal example follows the clinical example.

LIKE PULLING TEETH

Fay was a ninety-one-year-old toughie moved to a residential home when her sister died suddenly of pancreatic cancer in 2001. Fay had Alzheimer's, and hadn't had any of her own health-care practitioners for years, just seeing whomever her sister saw if anything came up. There were no records to rely on, and she couldn't remember any names of the practitioners she had seen. She resisted all caretaking, and her immediate response to all suggestions and invitations was "No!" She saw any care as fussing over her and intensely disliked being fussed over. She liked to be begged desperately to engage in activities—and would sometimes consent to take part if she were guilted enough. She wouldn't accept any new clothing unless it was donated or free.

The staff of Fay's residential facility pointed out to me that she left chewed-up food, especially meat, on her plate. I began to visit at mealtime to witness this for myself. It was true.

Fay had several resident friends who were more cognizant, and among them were Esther and Paula. The four of us sat and talked at times, and I turned the conversation to the dentist as many times as I dared. Esther and Paula caught on immediately, and chimed in about how they saw the dentist for prevention every six months, to which I replied, "Me too!" Fay then looked at each of us in amazement and said, "Really?" She contemplated aloud whether she should go, then concluded that nothing hurt so she didn't need to go. Esther and Paula picked up the banner and told her it might be too late by the time something hurt. We continued to work on convincing her for about four months.

During these four months, I'd been visiting more frequently to build our bond, and that had good results. She often wanted me to stay and sleep over, or told me she loved me as I went out the door. I did silly things she enjoyed, like visiting her on New Year's Eve wearing a lampshade for a hat. When she said she loved train rides, I brought videos of train rides and got her to go on the Minnesota Zephyr train in May.

It was time to make the dental move on her in June. I made the appointment and alerted the dentist to the retry of a failed attempt of over a year ago. Dr. Mike, the dentist and my friend, couldn't make it to my birthday party. The setup to woo Fay was that he wanted to have a little party for me in his office. He would offer "free" checkups to both of us for my birthday. Calming medication one hour before the appointed time should help too, we thought.

Fay refused to go with me. She wouldn't leave. (Another time when this happened for a planned outing, I got up and said that I was leaving then. She became alarmed, and jumped up to go with me.) After multiple refusals to go along, I said I was leaving and the staff immediately began the guilting, about how far I'd come and that this wasn't nice to do. Up she jumped, wanting to come along.

At the dental office, Dr. Mike examined my mouth very briefly by camera, trying to get Fay interested in the computer pictures. She wondered if teeth really were that color. She had no interest in seeing her own, though. Guessing how many teeth she had, and counting them was also a strike out. So Dr. Mike started making balloon gifts for my birthday. He made a balloon tiara, which I put on; a necklace, which I put on; and a flower for Fay to carry. That led to talk of great interest in flowers. She was sitting on a chair and I was on the edge of the dental chair. Dr. Mike went and got wall hangings of flowers, and we admired each as he brought them in. When he was out returning the last picture to its place, I looked at Fay and asked if there was a back on her chair. She said there was. I said my back was tired, and would she trade places with me? She said she sure would. When Dr. Mike returned and saw the switch, his eyes lit up and he said rather nonchalantly, "Fay, just lean back here and for Ellen's birthday let's you and me give her that free exam she'd like so much for you to have."

Fay said, "Okay," and promptly got into position.

The cajoling had taken well over half an hour. Dr. Mike's patience was remarkable. We had quietly whispered to each other several times during the process. Once I had said, "I give up."

"This is really a tough one," he had acknowledged, but he wouldn't give up. He used both linear and circular strategies, and adjusted his approach to what was working. Getting Fay to an improved state of dental health required a complex, improvised dance—and we found a way.

WHIRLING MOMENT

How does a fifty-year-old woman heal from and make peace with a system that has suppressed her essence most of her life? Very slowly. The experience of the individual represents the experience of the collective: as in the microcosm, so in the macrocosm. During my graduate studies in human development, I had ample opportunities to come to grips with the consequences of suppression and its results on historical personal and collective events. Whether we are speaking of a portion of one individual's lifetime (mine) or centuries of the hierarchical dominance visible in many cultures, healing is still needed and remains in process. Systems do not change overnight.

One opposite of suppressing is expressing. Expression comes in various forms, and it begets freedom. Dancing and writing are two types of expression. Writing the following was a part of healing the suppression.

Whirling Moment

Once upon a time, long long ago,
For a fleeting moment
I knew.

I knew
For a fleeting moment,
That creating was sacred—
A Process.

I knew for a fleeting moment,
That my body was a privilege
Not a commodity.

I knew
For a fleeting moment,
the Divinity of the Feminine...
Whirling humanity back to Source.

I glimpsed
For a fleeting moment,
The consciousness of an ascending Union...
Whirling humanity back to Source.

I fathomed the depth
I soared to the height
In that fleeting moment.

Then: Along came "Jones".
Big walking, big talking
Jones.
The Jones of my father and forefathers

Burned
The bones of my mother and foremothers
Whirling humanity away
Away from the depth
Away from the height
Away from the sanctity of the Union.

Oh grief! Through you
The lost has been found.

Oh tears! Through you
The tainted has been cleansed.

Oh anger! Through you
The external has been purged.

Oh persistence! Through you
The internal has been recognized.

Oh Love! Through you
The Eternal has been born

Again

Whirling humanity back to Source.
Whirling humanity back to Source.

Liberating the circular from suppression allows for the development of a more synergistic community that doesn't demand conformity. Strengthening the linear in a healthy way allows for dance as an expression of a life process that is deeply rooted. Integrated, we waltz, and sometimes stumble, through a flower garden full of diversity.

※ ※ ※

Selah:

stop and listen.

Study question: How have you and your health been affected when you have suppressed, and then expressed, yourself?

HEART RESPONSES	GUT RESPONSES	HEAD RESPONSES

13

Dancing On

Holistic philosophy concepts featured: unconditional acceptance, compassion, capacity for grace, inner peace, dynamic equilibrium, and helicy

We continue to change and grow and flower, individually, in partnerships, and as communities. This can be depicted by a holistic concept called helicy. The metaphor often used to depict emotional growth is "peeling the onion." This implies that one eventually arrives at the center with all the baggage peeled away, the growth more complete with each stripped layer. I find it more realistic to use the visual of the helicy concept here, and I like to give it a double meaning by spelling it *healicy* (see figure 15).

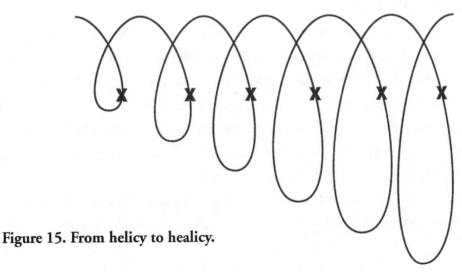

Figure 15. From helicy to healicy.

Each spiral (helix, helical) represents the passage of time and space. The X on each spiral represents the same issue, or baggage, we need to move past. The issue never disappears, it just comes up less often, and when it does, it is proportionally smaller. Eventually then, although an issue may be visible, it doesn't take up as much time or space as it once did. This feels like a more realistic and accepting way to view the imperfections of being human, and ride the waves of the spirals. It feels more like a dynamic equilibrium where everything is constantly changing in a way that allows for flow and movement while simultaneously maintaining a balance of sorts. It resists the possibility of equilibrium through stasis.

My formative years were spent in a fundamentalist religion, listening to hour-long hellfire-and-brimstone sermons at least once, sometimes three times, a week. It was an example of the hierarchy run rampant. I was indoctrinated into believing I was an awful person. When I couldn't heal that awful self-concept within that atmosphere, I looked for more healing environments.

My greatest healing experience came when I was doing an exercise in *The Twelve Steps—A Way Out: A Working Guide for Adult Children from Addictive and Other Dysfunctional Families* (17–26). I was working through step three: "Made a decision to turn our will and our lives over to the care of God as we understood God." The purpose of the exercise is to arrive at one's own understanding of God.

The first part of the exercise calls for you to divide your life into decades and, for each decade, list the names of people who were significantly helpful. You are to think of them as a light at the end of a tunnel. The next part of the exercise is to list the characteristics that made each of them a light for you. Then that list of characteristics should be copied separately, without names, onto a piece of paper. With soft and soothing music playing, you reflect on the list. You reflect on the characteristics you identified as your own individual understanding of God.

As the music played, I closed my eyes and reviewed the list in my heart and head. I began to weep softly as a light appeared and hovered about a foot in front of my forehead. It seemed to be reassuring me that it would be with me and always offer unconditional acceptance, unconditional love and compassion, peace, and grace. An inner peace came over me and has been with me ever since. The X on my helical spirals is still the residue of my childhood conviction that I'm an awful person, but I've moved far beyond the self-destructive behaviors that for many years manifested that belief. This experience has been key in healing the negative effects of hierarchal thinking and actions in my life.

We tend to reflect how we feel about ourselves in the ways we treat others. It's especially crucial to be aware of this tendency when working with vulnerable people, otherwise abuse, which includes neglect, easily occurs. Neglecting or abusing others can be largely unconscious when we are not conscious of treating ourselves with neglect or abuse, when we don't know there is any other way. If we see ourselves as inferior or superior, then we operate in that model with others. This is the linear or hierarchical model. When we see ourselves and others as equal, then we operate out of the circular model.

In twenty-two years as a nurse care manager, half of my caseload included vulnerable adults with some form of dementia. The following clinical example is about being present with unconditional acceptance, love, compassion, inner peace, and grace. Because this was given to me through the exercise I describe above, I've been able to give it to others on occasion. The personal illustration that follows may be difficult for some, who might view it as heretical.

SHARING HEART SPACE

For nine years, Kay had twenty-four-hour help in her home. As a very sociable person, she was starved for more companionship than her caregivers could provide. Her friends didn't know how to relate to her at the latter stage of her disease. She was moved to a house where she had five peers with Alzheimer's and her final two years were more pleasant. She knew my voice and face well after many years with her. One day I visited, and she was very busy moving papers around and around on a table. She appeared to be in somewhat of a trance. She couldn't hear my greeting. She couldn't feel my touch. I knew if I could get eye contact, though, we could connect.

I joined her. I began pushing the papers around and around on the table. Her motion stopped briefly, then resumed. Her eyes were intent on the papers. She had allowed me to join her at that point. I knew I had to enhance the experience for her to get her to connect with me. I looked around and saw two throw pillows. I brought them to the table. I put some papers under and on top of one pillow, and then put the second pillow on top of all that. I began moving that stack around, sometimes pulling papers out and putting them back under the pillows. She stopped, grinned, and then finally looked at me. We connected. She held my hands and we walked together, away from the table and the trance, into our shared heart space.

MY NICE CREED

To continue healing I had to expand the Twelve Step exercise further. I needed to come to terms with some indoctrinated notions that were troubling me. One year I was reviewing some of the teachings from my past. I came upon the Nicene Creed. I struggled with its ingrained hierarchy, and decided I needed to write my own creed. I called it "My Nice Creed." At first, I started it with "I believe." Then I read something written by Father Richard Rohr, a Catholic priest. "Outer spiritual believing tends to say, 'Only here' or 'only there,' while authentic inner knowing tends to say, 'Always and everywhere.' We start elitist and we end egalitarian" (6).

After reading this, I changed the beginning of "My Nice Creed" from "I believe" to "I know."

I know
1. That I was born originally blessed, as a spark of the Divine.
2. That I am good. I am not so awful that someone had to die for me.
3. That I make mistakes and therefore am a perfect human being; that is, I am imperfect, which is what it takes to be a perfect human being.
4. That great teachers in many spiritual traditions died, were murdered, were assassinated, or were martyred defending their messages of love, peace, and compassion.
5. That these great teachers wanted followers to believe in their messages, not in them. I think they would be horrified at how we have used them as persons to cause separation in the world. If we are not to shoot the messenger, then we are not to worship the messenger either.
6. That each person's guru is within.
7. That early church leaders saw how love and interdependence caused loss of their power and control. This threatened them. Therefore, they came up with a creed based on fear to keep their power and control over the people. This is diametrically opposed to the original messages of love, peace, and compassion.
8. That a nonliteral interpretation of the sacraments provides a deep, universal, and positive experience. In the sacrament of communion, the wine represents the Holy Spirit or the Divine Feminine, and the bread represents the Word or the Divine Masculine. Therefore, the Divine Feminine and the Divine Masculine are both to be taken in equally. The sacrament of baptism is about transformation. Therefore, baptism can take a variety of forms, since each person experiences transformation in his or her own way.

9. That when someone wants me to believe as they do, it is a form of violence. I feel anger, fear, and violation. They are projecting onto me the anger, fear, and sense of violation that are within themselves. Their desire to have me believe as they do is a commentary on their pain more than it is a judgment about my beliefs.

10. That Sophia is the inhalation, the *yin*, of the Breath of Life. In Greek and Hebrew the word for *breath* and the word for *spirit* are the same word. Sophia embraces and receives, focusing on the inner, the circular, inclusiveness. Spirit and energy are often visualized in swirls and spirals. When young Sophia dances, she is often depicted as twirling. Without Sophia, focus is limited to the outer. Then swirls and spirals lose their energy and shape shift to the linear, which must have constant input from tributaries or transformers to maintain energy, whereas swirls and spirals energetically increase on their own. Without Sophia, we perish.

11. That any talk of a Higher Power that is not comforting or compassionate is a lie. The source of all addictions is a deep yearning for union with the spiritual.

12. That heaven and hell exist in the here and now. Our choices create which one we live in on this Earth. A loving Higher Power would enfold all of us in the afterlife and does not condemn us for actions based on deep psychological wounds perpetuated by the confusing, power-hungry, and thus aspiritual, hierarchy.

13. That there is a spiritual lesson in all forms of illness and disease, or dis-ease.

14. That the soul needs beauty just as the lungs need air. The service of beauty is to purify, to heal, to reveal the divine, and thus to transform. Transformation is a forever dance.

15. That nature provides the model for living meaningful, connected lives. We are to flow and caress like water, honor all the seasons of our lives as we birth and grow and age and sage, play like dolphins, and provide each other with warmth and community like sheep.

Perhaps the traditional church could regain some of its followers if there were less emphasis on the hierarchy among the leaders of the church, and more focus on and attention to the holistic concepts featured in this chapter and this creed. These concepts are love, unconditional acceptance, compassion, capacity for grace, inner peace, dynamic equilibrium, and the constant changes of helicy/healicy.

☙☙☙

Selah:

stop and listen.

Study question: Is it easier to practice unconditional acceptance, compassion, grace, and inner peace with a child or an adult? How so?

HEART RESPONSES	GUT RESPONSES	HEAD RESPONSES

Epilogue

I attempt to teach what I most need to learn. I am one year older than the Baby Boomers. The Baby Boomers and the Silent Generation before them are more indoctrinated to hierarchical thinking than the current Gen Xers, Gen Yers, and Millennials seem to be. It's inspiring to see how some of the children born to the Gen Xers and Gen Yers are more familiar with the concepts of the circular paradigm. An idiomatic phrase has emerged from the younger generations in the recent years: "It is what it is." I was taken aback when I first heard it. In those few words, I hear a decreased need for control and power—and by extension, less adherence to hierarchical thinking.

When I learned about the form of the mandala, and as I became more conscious of the characteristics of the emerging circular paradigm, I saw both demonstrated all around me. The fifteen-ton, fifty-foot-wide electromagnet—an object capable of impressive force—that was moved from New York to suburban Chicago in July 2013 is similar in form to the mandala. Pictures of almost all UFOs show circular objects. Much ancient architecture is circular. The Native American medicine wheel and most crop circles are round.

Several people who offered feedback on figure 12, which depicts a satellite, had traveled to ancient sites in Greece and surrounding areas. They saw similarity between the illustration and the amphitheaters there. They saw the seating area for the amphitheaters as the equivalent of the solar panels and small, course-correcting jets for the satellite. They saw the mandala as the round grassy area where the speakers would stand.

When it comes to nature, flowers aren't the only manifestation of the merger of the linear and circular. Look at the trees. The branches are round in circumference and linear as they reach for the sky. The trunk is linear and the shape of the canopy is usually circular. A swan's neck is long and linear, yet round. Likewise for the giraffe, and other animals and birds—though it's less obvious for those with shorter necks. In our bodies, nerves, blood vessels, and most bones are long and linear yet round. Raindrops are depicted as round, and usually fall in a linear manner. Pictures depict big waves in the ocean ascending linearly and then curling at the top of the wave before falling. Linear rays come from the round sun.

We could even find parallels with sports and games. A round golf ball is hit with a linear club. A round baseball is hit with a linear bat that is also rounded. A cribbage board is usually linear with round holes for linear round pegs. Linear BB guns shoot round pellets.

The letters of our alphabet are composed of both linear and rounded lines, as are our numerals. Linear pages in notebooks are kept in place with round holes and clasps or spirals. Linear pieces of tape come on a round roll. Linear pens and pencils are round.

The circular paradigm is all around us—pun intended. It takes a linear left-brain choice to circularly embrace a healthy merger of the two. Making this choice daily is the kind of work and calling that characterizes true partnership. I'm committed to continue learning this dance, and I invite you to dance with me.

WORKS CONSULTED

American Holistic Nurse Association (AHNA), American Nurses Association (ANA), 2013. *Holistic Nursing: Scope and Standards of Practice,* second edition. Silver Springs, MD: NursesBooks.org.

Argüelles, José, and Miriam Argüelles. 1972. *Mandala.* Boston: Shambhala.

Artress, Lauren. 2006. *Walking a Sacred Path.* New York, NY: Riverhead Books.

Baines, Barry K. 2002. *Ethical Wills: Putting Your Values on Paper.* Cambridge, MA: Da Capo Press.

Buber, Martin. 1970. *I and Thou.* Translated by Walter Kaufmann. New York: Simon and Schuster.

Buchbinder, Amnon. 2013. "Out of Our Heads: Philip Shepherd on the Brain in Our Belly." *The Sun,* 448, 7-14.

Capacchione, Lucia. 2001. *The Power of Your Other Hand.* Franklin Lakes, NJ: Career Press.

Covey, Stephen R. 2004. *The 7 Habits of Highly Effective People: Powerful Lessons in Personal Change.* New York: Free Press.

———. 2011. *The 3rd Alternative: Solving Life's Most Difficult Problems.* New York: Free Press.

Dossey, Barbara Montgomery. 2013. "Nursing: Integral, Integrative, and Holistic – Local to Global." In Barbara Montgomery Dossey and Lynn Keegan, eds. *Holistic Nursing: A Handbook for Practice, sixth edition,* 3-57. Burlington, MA: Jones and Bartlett Learning.

Eisler, Riane. 1987. *The Chalice and the Blade: Our History, Our Future.* San Francisco: Harper.

Eisler, Riane, and David Loye. 1990. *The Partnership Way.* San Francisco: Harper.

Erickson, Helen C., Evelyn Tomlin, and Mary Ann P. Swain. 1983. *Modeling and Role-Modeling: A Theory and Paradigm for Nursing.* Cedar Park, TX: EST.

Fox, Matthew. 1990. *A Spirituality Named Compassion.* San Francisco: Harper.

———. 1998. "Education as Lighting a Fire: A Commencement Address by Matthew Fox." *Original Blessing,* 1, 1-5.

Friends in Recovery. 1989. The Twelve Steps—*A Way Out: A Working Guide for Adult Children from Addictive and Other Dysfunctional Families,* revised edition. San Diego, CA: Recovery Publications.

Frisch, Noreen Cavan. 2013. "Nursing Theory in Holistic Nursing Practice." In Barbara Dossey and Lynn Keegan, eds. *Holistic Nursing: A Handbook for Practice,* sixth edition, 117-28. Burlington, MA: Jones and Bartlett Learning.

Fuller, Buckminster R. In "A Tribute to R. Buckminster Fuller, 1895–1983." Retrieved from http://www.endalldisease.com/spectacular-quotes-from-buckminster-fuller/.

Gendlin, Eugene T. 1978. *Focusing*. New York, NY: Bantam Books.

George, Bill. 2011. "Leadership Skills Start with Self Awareness." *Star Tribune*, February 27, 2011, D3.

Hogan, Eve Eschner. 2003. *Way of the Winding Path: A Map for the Labyrinth of Life*. Ashland, OR: White Cloud Press.

Jung, Carl Gustav, and Marie-Lousie von Franz. 1964. "The Process of Individuation." In Carl Gustav Jung, Marie-Louise von Franz, et al. *Man and His Symbols*. 158-229. Garden City, NJ: Doubleday.

Levine, Peter A., with A. Frederick. 1997. *Waking the Tiger: Healing Trauma*. Berkeley, CA: North Atlantic Books.

Mackay, Harvey. 2012. "Difference Between Self-Serving Leaders and Servant Leaders." *Star Tribune*, October 1, 2012, D3.

Manaster, Guy J., and Raymond J. Corsini. 1982. *Individual Psychology: Theory and Practice*. Itasca, IL: F. E. Peacock.

Miller, A. 2005. "African Wisdom for Life." Calendar. Nairobi: Pauline's Publications Africa.

Nair, Keshavan. 1997. *A Higher Standard of Leadership: Lessons from the Life of Gandhi*. San Francisco: Berrett-Koehler.

Rath, Tom. 2007. *StrengthsFinder 2.0*. New York: Gallop Press.

Rohr, Richard. 2013. *Immortal Diamond: The Search for Our True Self*. San Francisco: Jossey-Bass.

Schaef, Anne Wilson. 1987. *When Society Becomes an Addict*. San Francisco: Harper & Row.

———. 1988. *The Addictive Organization*. San Francisco: Harper & Row.

Shepherd, Philip. 2010. *New Self, New World*. Berkeley, CA: North Atlantic Books.

Skorucak, Anton. "The Science of Tears." Retrieved from http://www.scienceiq.com/facts/scienceoftears.cfm.

Townsend, Mary. 2013. "Holistic Leadership." Beginnings, 32 (6), 2-17.

Webster's Encyclopedic Unabridged Dictionary of the English Language, revised edition. 1996. "Mandala." New York, NY: Random House Gramercy Books, 870.

WORKSHEET

The following worksheet is for your use of the mandala or circular paradigm. You'll want to enlarge it to a usable size, the smallest of which is eleven by seventeen inches.

Acknowledgments

Special thanks to Helen Erickson for insisting I write this book, and for her steady encouragement. I am deeply grateful to Ellen Schultz and Mary Johnson for their solid support, explanations, and inspiration during this process. All three are such talented, thoughtful, and accessible professors of nursing.

Oh, how I have missed the continuation of the early support of the late Professor Kathleen O'Donovan, who told me that it's my job as an inspired introvert to get under the skin of others and make them itch! Her dear friend Professor Emeritus Steve Simmons valiantly stepped forward and played a key role as my writing coach. Without him, I wouldn't have believed in the potential strength of the stories to illustrate the holistic concepts I discuss.

Fellow nurses Susan Arnold, Deb Egerdahl, Sandy Field, and Stacy Miorana provided vital additional perspectives from our shared profession.

Jennelle Donnay, as a comrade in dance, finally convinced me that the nursing theory featured herein was relevant to the circular template about which you have read.

Barbara Bobrowitz noted how I had unconsciously incorporated the fêng shui ba-gua (energy map) into the template and thereafter provided helpful fêng shui expertise and advice.

Bettie Seitzer gave me a middle manager's perspective on the application of the circular template to the business world.

Ron Moor and Ginny Cone provided explanations and opportunities for applications of the template that I hadn't considered.

Tom Vetter contributed scientific information that made so many pieces fall into place. The synchronicity with which this happened always amazed me.

Niece Amber Hernley Larkin applied the template to her children and verified my theory that this could make a great digital tool for documenting the developmental growth of a child.

My neighbors Dennis and Mary Caskey believed in this project and provided insights from the realms of business and psychology.

Neighbor Mike Guimond models how a man can very effectively integrate these circular concepts into his relationships with men, women, and children.

Graphic Designer Penni St. Hilaire of Allegra took my pencil sketches and digitally transformed them into audible audience gasps.

Lily Coyle, publishing director at Beaver's Pond Press, knows how to profoundly encourage a new author. Halfway into our first meeting, she stated, "I want to see this book published before I reach my dotage, because this is the kind of care I want." Three hours later, I received an email stating she had read the entire manuscript already, after intending to just peek at it.

Katy Jo Turner, project manager at Beaver's Pond Press, stood with me and supported me through thick and thin, and succeeded in her goal to make this fun for me.

Editor Wendy Weckwerth, with brilliant editing, provided a smoother flow to the manuscript and clarified its message.

Designer Laura Drew, with wizard-like intuition, gifted this work with her magic wand.

Alicia Ester was the proofreader version of Catfish Hunter. She cleaned up the dregs and saved the game.

And finally, Moses came through the ages. He showed me how to part the roiling Red Sea of edits, and loaned me his Dramamine staff to smite the clicker that said to "accept all changes." Then with a clear path, he walked with me step by step as we took one edit at a time.

To all of you, I am most grateful. Many thanks for blessing this work with your rich contributions.

ABOUT THE AUTHOR

ELLEN SWANSON is retired from a forty-six-year nursing career that included ortho-rehab, mental health, operating room, and care management on a clinical level. In the nonclinical area, her career included teaching at her alma mater as well as consulting, administration, and supervision in hospitals. She also had a private practice in holistic nursing for fifteen years, utilizing guided imagery, breath work, and spiritual concepts from the treatment programs for addictions. She is a certified holistic nurse and has studied Healing Touch, Reiki, yoga, tai chi, breath work, and qigong.

She was advised not to retire from, but to retire to. She has chosen to retire to three projects. The first is interpretive dance, which she calls TranscenDance. She offers programs (not performances) that she calls "Dance and Dialogue." The second project is a booklet on Alzheimer's entitled *Lessons for Dancing the Long Goodbye: Seven Steps to Making Peace with Alzhiemer's.* The third project is the mandala labyrinth she describes in *Heart, Gut, Head: Creating a Healthier Hierarchy* which came out of a desire to portray a less hierarchical way of living.

Ellen received her BSN from Goshen College in Goshen, Indiana, in 1968, her certification in holistic nursing in 1998, and her MA in human development from St. Mary's University, Minneapolis Campus, in 1999. She currently serves on the Council for the Minnesota Holistic Nurses Association.